Everyday Mathematics®

Skills Link™

Cumulative Practice Sets

Everyday Mathematics®

Skills Link™

Cumulative Practice Sets

EVERYDAY LEARNING®

Chicago, Illinois

Everyday Learning Development Staff

Editorial: Rosemary Baker, Steve Mico, Michael Murphy, Adam Sugerman
Design: Jess Schaal
Production: Annette Davis, Norma Underwood

Additional Credits

Patrick Carroll *(editorial)*
Darrel A. Trulson *(production)*

ISBN 1-57039-742-2

2 3 4 5 6 7 8 9 CU 02 01 00 99

Contents

Mixed Practice Set 1

Solve.

1. 2×4

2. $14 - 7$

3. $84 - 27$

4. $300 + 500$

5. $3581 - 1993$

6. $304 + 832$

7. $4315 + 2127$

8. 9×0

9. $(50 + 20) \times 4$

10. $27 - (5 \times 4)$

11. $240 + 154 + 122$

12. $525 + 440 + 120$

---

13. *Copy the place-value puzzle on your paper. Then use the clues to complete the puzzle.*

1000s	100s	10s	1s

- Write the result of $21 \div 7$ in the ones place.
- Multiply 8×9. Subtract 65. Write the result in the tens place.
- Double the number in the ones place. Write the result in the thousands place.
- Divide 18 by 6. Add 5 and write the result in the hundreds place.

Make a name-collection box for each number listed below. Use as many different numbers and operations as you can.

Example:

19
$(6 \times 3) + 1$
$38 \div 2$
$(40 - 25) + 4$

14. 38

15. 7

16. 218

Mixed Practice Set

*Complete the **What's My Rule?** tables.*

1.

Rule	in	out
out = in × 3	3	9
	4	12
	7	
	11	
	15	

2.

Rule	in	out
	8	4
	14	7
		9
	24	
	36	18

Solve.

3. The Coffee-to-Go Cafe uses about 5 gallons of milk per day.

  a. About how many gallons of milk does it use in a week (7 days)?

  b. How many gallons in 5 weeks?

  c. How many in one year (52 weeks)?

4. 180
  − 172

5. 684
  − 348

6. 74
  + 27

7. 5101
  − 540

8. 500
  − 290

9. 402
  + 293

10. 3418
  + 6583

11. 49
  − 6

12. 120
  − 30

Mixed Practice Set 2 *(continued)*

Complete the frames-and-arrows problems.

Examples: *(with one rule)*

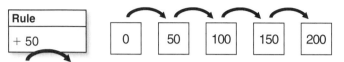

(with two rules)

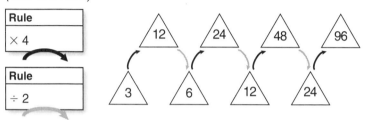

13.

14.

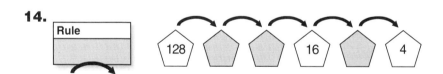

15.

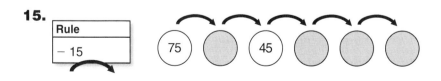

Mixed Practice Set 3

Write the number models with parentheses and solve.

1. Add 15 to the difference of 105 and 70.

2. Subtract the sum of 8 and 3 from 18.

3. Add 9 to the difference of 50 and 16.

4. Subtract the sum of 81 and 42 from 338.

Rewrite the number models with parentheses to make them correct.

5. $6 \times 8 - 3 = 45$

6. $22 = 8 + 3 \times 2$

7. $33 - 15 - 6 = 24$

8. $54 - 10 + 8 = 52$

9. $3 \times 8 + 2 \times 11 = 46$

10. $30 = 4 \times 6 + 6$

11. $2 \times 2 + 7 \times 8 = 60$

12. $489 = 5 \times 25 + 75 - 11$

Solve.

13. Mrs. Brown's class kept track of the number of hours they spent reading each day. The graph shows the number of hours the students spent reading Monday through Wednesday.

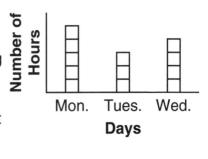

a. How many more hours did they read on Monday than on Tuesday?

b. What is the average number of hours they spent reading in a day?

c. How many total hours do you think they would read, Monday through Friday? Explain.

Mixed Practice Set 4

1. In basketball, what is the total score for five 3-point baskets and nine 2-point baskets? Write a number sentence using multiplication and parentheses.

Find the area, in square units, of each rectangle and then write the number model.

> **Reminder:** Area = length (*l*) × width (*w*)

Example: 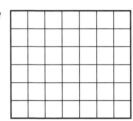 6 × 7 = 42

2.   **3.**

Write the digit in the hundredths place for each of the following.

4. 5.925   **5.** 1.043   **6.** 8.100   **7.** 0.280   **8.** 3.313

Write 2 multiplication and 2 division facts for the following groups of numbers:

9. 6, 7, and 42   **10.** 3, 9, and 27   **11.** 4, 8, and 32

12. 5, 9, and 45   **13.** 2, 8, and 16   **14.** 4, 7, and 28

Mixed Practice Set 4 *(continued)*

Solve.

15. $120 - \blacksquare = 30$ **16.** $82 + 17$

17. $70 + 26$ **18.** $40 - 17$

19. $16 - 8$ **20.** 9×9

21.
$$\begin{array}{r} 87 \\ -\ 36 \\ \hline \end{array}$$

22.
$$\begin{array}{r} 333 \\ -\ 141 \\ \hline \end{array}$$

23.
$$\begin{array}{r} 37 \\ \times\ 8 \\ \hline \end{array}$$

24.
$$\begin{array}{r} 1114 \\ +\ 3455 \\ \hline \end{array}$$

25.
$$\begin{array}{r} 120 \\ \times\ 50 \\ \hline \end{array}$$

26.
$$\begin{array}{r} 207 \\ 521 \\ +\ 131 \\ \hline \end{array}$$

27. Joy wants to have enough balloons for her 22 party guests. How many packages of 6 does she need?

28. Larry has a large pizza to share with 3 friends. If the pizza is divided into 16 slices, how many slices will each person, including Larry, get?

29. If four more friends join Larry and the others, how many slices will each person get?

Mixed Practice Set 5

Complete the frames-and-arrows problem.

1.

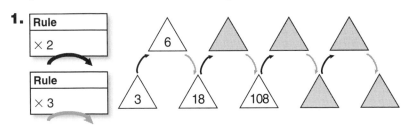

Rule
× 2

Rule
× 3

2. In baseball, the bases on the diamond are placed exactly 90 ft apart.

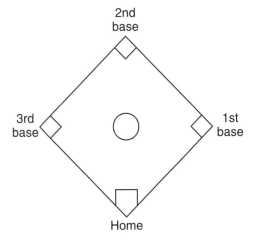

2nd
base

3rd
base

1st
base

Home

a. If a batter hits a home run, how many feet does she run?

b. If there are runners on first and third when a batter hits a home run, what is the total distance all three players run?

3. Write the following number in digits: eight thousand, four hundred twenty-one.

4. Write the words for 1603.

Mixed Practice Set 6

For each Fact Minute below, do as many problems as you can in that minute. You can ask someone to time you.

Fact Minute 1	Fact Minute 2	Fact Minute 3
1. $18 \div 6$	**16.** 4×8	**31.** 9×6
2. 7×7	**17.** $36 \div 6$	**32.** $24 \div 4$
3. 4×5	**18.** 5×9	**33.** 2×7
4. $54 \div 9$	**19.** 8×4	**34.** 8×7
5. 3×4	**20.** 3×8	**35.** 3×7
6. $64 \div 8$	**21.** $48 \div 6$	**36.** $27 \div 3$
7. 6×8	**22.** 7×4	**37.** 7×5
8. 6×6	**23.** $28 \div 7$	**38.** 3×6
9. 9×9	**24.** 2×5	**39.** $8 \div 4$
10. $49 \div 7$	**25.** 6×3	**40.** 4×3
11. 9×4	**26.** $32 \div 4$	**41.** 9×8
12. 7×9	**27.** 6×7	**42.** $63 \div 9$
13. 6×2	**28.** 4×7	**43.** 9×5
14. $56 \div 7$	**29.** $20 \div 5$	**44.** $15 \div 3$
15. 7×6	**30.** 8×9	**45.** 2×8

Write answers on a separate sheet of paper.   Use with or after Unit 1.

Mixed Practice Set 6 (continued)

Lightbulbs
4-pack $1.07

Tissues
$0.99

Batteries
4-pack $2.19

Transparent Tape
$0.84

Ballpoint Pen
$0.27

VCR Tape
$2.79

46. John must buy supplies for his company. He needs five lightbulbs, four boxes of tissues, and six rolls of transparent tape. How much money will he need for these supplies?

47. Ms. Larson has four dollars. How many pens can she buy?

48. Judy and Sarah are going to videotape their school's pageant. They need eight batteries and two VCR tapes for the camera. They have ten dollars. Do they have enough money to buy what they need? What is the difference between the money they have and the money they need?

49. About how much is each of the lightbulbs in the 4-pack?

50. About how much is each of the batteries in the 4-pack?

Mixed Practice Set 7

Solve.

1. 80 ÷ 8 = ■   **2.** 30 × 80 = ■

3. 800 = 8 × ■   **4.** 4 × 400 = ■

5. 30 × ■ = 1500   **6.** ■ ÷ 1000 = 8

7. 1400 ÷ 700 = ■   **8.** 28 × ■ = 560

9. ■ ÷ 70 = 70   **10.** 6 × 30 = ■

11. 4500 ÷ ■ = 5   **12.** 9 × 90 = ■

13. How much money, without tax, will I need for 3 boxes of crackers that cost $1.59 each?

14. How many dollars in 18 five-dollar bills?

15. If 1 block is 200 meters long, how far will you run in 7 blocks?

Write numbers for the fractional parts shown in each picture.

Example:  $\frac{6}{12}$ or $\frac{1}{2}$

16.    **17.**

18.    **19.**

Mixed Practice Set 8

Solve.

1. 6 × 6

2. 12 × 6

3. 7 × 5

4. 10 × 7

5. 11 × 4

6. 9 × 9

7. 6 × 8

8. 7 × 5

9. 9 × 11

10. 2 × 12

11. 11 × 8

12. 8 × 12

13. 10 × 11

14. 8 × 4

15. 60 ÷ 10

16. 9 × 5

17. 7 × 11

18. 12 × 7

19. 16 ÷ 8

20. 60 ÷ 12

21. *Use the clues to complete the place-value puzzle.*

- Divide 72 by 6. Subtract 4 and write the result in the ones place.

- Double the number in the ones place and divide by 8. Write the result in the tens place.

- Multiply 9 × 10. Subtract 83. Write the result in the hundreds place.

- Halve the number in the tens place. Multiply by 3 and write the result in the thousands place.

- Divide 27 by the number in the thousands place. Write the result in the ten-thousands place.

10,000s	1000s	100s	10s	1s

Mixed Practice Set 8 *(continued)*

Solve.

22. 2654
  + 4783

23. 6355
  + 1829

24. 16
  × 4

25. 180
  × 7

26. 196
  × 0

27. 32.1
  + 18.7

28. 1.25
  + 6.43

29. 8.40
  − 5.01

30. 11
  × 9

31. 85
  − 38

32. 205
   832
  + 117

33. 8362
  − 4170

Use digits to write the following numbers.

34. twenty-four thousand, nine hundred sixty-eight

35. seventy six thousand, six hundred fourteen

36. six thousand, nine hundred two

Write the words for the following numbers.

37. 12,743

38. 8,054

39. 69,231

40. 4,782

Mixed Practice Set 9

Rewrite the number sentences with parentheses to make them correct.

1. $6 \times 11 - 7 = 59$ **2.** $2.2 = 8 - 3 + 2.8$

3. $330 - 150 - 60 = 240$ **4.** $18 = 2 \times 5.4 + 3.6$

5. $7 \times 2.1 + 5 \times 12 = 74.7$ **6.** $230 = 4 \times 60 - 10$

7. $3 \times 9 + 3 - 4 = 32$ **8.** $584 = 11 \times 50 + 34$

---

*Complete the **What's My Rule?** tables.*

9. Rule: out = in × 20

in	out
9	180
12	240
15	
25	
100	

10. Rule:

in	out
7	3.5
10	6.5
	10.5
16.5	
20.5	17

11. Rule:

in	out
80	20
160	
	90
2400	
4800	1200

12. Rule: out = in × 10

in	out
3	
6	
	90
	120
15	

Mixed Practice Set 10

In each set of problems below, do as many exercises as you can in one minute. Ask someone to time you.

Problem Set 1	Problem Set 2	Problem Set 3
1. 10×6	**16.** 2×5	**31.** $54 \div 9$
2. 7×11	**17.** 9×11	**32.** 12×2
3. $48 \div 4$	**18.** $110 \div 10$	**33.** 12×5
4. 2×9	**19.** 8×4	**34.** 12×3
5. 10×4	**20.** 11×10	**35.** $121 \div 11$
6. $90 \div 9$	**21.** 6×12	**36.** 60×5
7. 5×11	**22.** 11×11	**37.** 8×7
8. 10×12	**23.** 12×11	**38.** $144 \div 12$
9. $49 \div 7$	**24.** 4×7	**39.** $8 \div 4$
10. 4×12	**25.** 12×16	**40.** $33 \div 3$
11. 7×8	**26.** $63 \div 7$	**41.** $42 \div 7$
12. $63 \div 9$	**27.** 8×6	**42.** $81 \div 9$
13. $45 \div 5$	**28.** 3×3	**43.** $32 \div 8$
14. 6×7	**29.** $45 \div 9$	**44.** $18 \div 9$
15. $18 \div 2$	**30.** $16 \div 4$	**45.** 7×3

Mixed Practice Set 10 *(continued)*

46. *Use the clues to complete the place-value puzzle.*

- Divide 88 by 11. Add 1 and write the result in the thousands place.
- Double the number in the thousands place and divide by 3. Write the result in the tens place.
- Multiply 4 × 12. Subtract 42. Write the result in the hundreds place.
- Divide 63 by the number in the thousands place. Write the result in the ones place.
- Halve the number in the tens place. Add 1 and write the result in the ten-thousands place.

10,000s	1000s	100s	10s	1s

Solve.

47. $1.20 × 5 = ■

48. 24 = 8 × ■

49. 9.2 + 6.3 = ■

50. 3 × ■ = $1.80

51. ■ ÷ 1200 = 5

52. 14.0 − 7.4 = ■

53. 18 × ■ = 36

54. ■ ÷ 180 = 2

Make a name-collection box for each number below. Use as many different numbers and operations as you can.

Example:

14.2
71 ÷ 5
7.1 × 2
20 − 5.8
(3.5 × 2) + (9.2 − 2)

55. 38.7

56. 7049

57. 8.12

58. 1005

59. 20.2

60. 706

Mixed Practice Set 11

Use digits to write the following numbers:

1. sixteen thousand, five hundred forty-seven

2. eight and two-tenths

3. seven and nine-tenths

Write the words for the following numbers:

4. 21,894

5. 14.1

6. 48,563

7. 903

Complete the frames-and-arrows problems.

8.

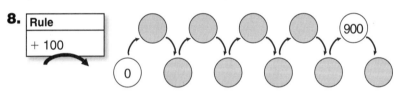

9.

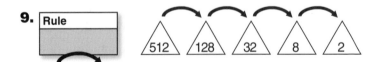

10.

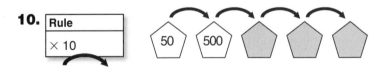

Mixed Practice Set 12

Complete the missing factors.

1. $7 \times \blacksquare = 21$

2. $\blacksquare \times 4 = 36$

3. $\blacksquare \times 8 = 64$

4. $12 \times \blacksquare = 96$

5. $400 \times \blacksquare = 3600$

6. $\blacksquare \times 5 = 350$

7. $9 \times \blacksquare = 810$

8. $\blacksquare \times 6 = 660$

Estimate the total cost.

9. 12 rulers that cost $1.05 each

10. 4 scissors that cost $0.69 each

11. 7 books that cost $3.45 each

Solve.

12.
$$\begin{array}{r} 440 \\ 115 \\ + 711 \\ \hline \end{array}$$

13.
$$\begin{array}{r} 79 \\ + 28 \\ \hline \end{array}$$

14.
$$\begin{array}{r} 784 \\ - 426 \\ \hline \end{array}$$

15.
$$\begin{array}{r} 230 \\ \times 8 \\ \hline \end{array}$$

16.
$$\begin{array}{r} 112 \\ \times 9 \\ \hline \end{array}$$

17.
$$\begin{array}{r} 263 \\ 357 \\ + 198 \\ \hline \end{array}$$

18.
$$\begin{array}{r} 4315 \\ - 78 \\ \hline \end{array}$$

19.
$$\begin{array}{r} 24 \\ - 11 \\ \hline \end{array}$$

20.
$$\begin{array}{r} 78 \\ \times 4 \\ \hline \end{array}$$

21.
$$\begin{array}{r} 625 \\ - 36 \\ \hline \end{array}$$

22.
$$\begin{array}{r} 482 \\ \times 2 \\ \hline \end{array}$$

23.
$$\begin{array}{r} 96 \\ \times 3 \\ \hline \end{array}$$

Mixed Practice Set 12 *(continued)*

Complete the frames-and-arrows problems.

24.
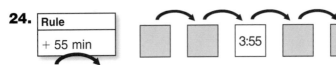

Rule
+ 55 min

3:55

25.
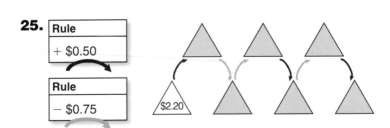

Rule
+ $0.50

Rule
− $0.75

$2.20

26.
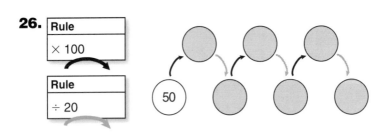

Rule
× 100

Rule
÷ 20

50

27.
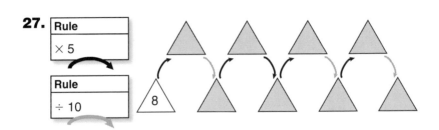

Rule
× 5

Rule
÷ 10

8

Mixed Practice Set 13

1. How many pieces of fruit are there?

2. What fraction of the fruit are apples?

3. What fraction of the fruit are pears?

4. What fraction of the fruit are bananas?

Solve.

5. 67
  × 4

6. 53
  × 8

7. 84 ÷ 3

8. 675
  × 6

9. 8229
  + 3160

10. 7583
  − 5432

11. 3499
  × 0

12. 673
  − 64

13. 467
  + 185

14. 320
  × 8

15. 560 ÷ 8

16. 8524
  − 1996

Mixed Practice Set 14

1. Four people are going to share $68 equally.
  a. How many $10 bills does each person get?
  b. How many dollars are left to share?
  c. From the money that remains, how many $1 bills does each person get?
  d. What is the total number of dollars each person gets?
  e. Number model: $4 \times 17 = $ ■

2. Seven people are going to share $112 equally.
  a. How many $100 bills does each person get?
  b. From the money that remains, how many $10 bills does each person get?
  c. How many dollars are left to share?
  d. From the money that remains, how many $1 bills does each person get?
  e. What is the total number of dollars each person gets?
  f. Write a number model for this problem.

3. Six people are going to share $681 equally.
  a. How many $100 bills does each person get?
  b. How many dollars are left to share?
  c. From the money that remains, how many $10 bills does each person get?
  d. How many dollars are left to share?
  e. From the money that remains, how many $1 bills does each person get?
  f. How many dollars are left over?
  g. If the leftover money is shared equally, how many cents does each person get?
  h. What is the total amount of money each person gets?
  i. Write a number model for this problem.

Mixed Practice Set 14 (continued)

Write the amounts.

4. (Q)(Q)(Q)(Q)(Q)(D)(D)(N)(N)(N)(P)(P)(P)

5. | $1 | | $1 | (Q)(Q)(Q)(D)(D)(D)(D)
(N)(P)(P)

6. | $5 | | $5 | | $5 | | $1 | (Q)(N)(N)(N)

7. | $100 | | $20 | | $20 | | $5 | | $1 | | $1 | | $1 |
(Q)

Fill in the missing numbers on the number lines.

8.

9   17   ■   33   ■   ■   ■   65

9.

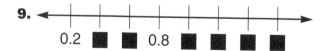

0.2   ■   ■   0.8   ■   ■   ■   ■

10.

$\frac{1}{7}$ $\frac{2}{7}$ ■ $\frac{4}{7}$ ■   ■   1   ■   ■

11.

■   8   ■   16   ■   ■   28   ■   ■   ■   ■

Mixed Practice Set 15

Who am I?

1. Clue 1: I am less than 10.

    Clue 2: I am an odd number.

    Clue 3: If you turn me upside down, I am an even number.

2. Clue 1: I am less than 100.

    Clue 2: The sum of my digits is 8.

    Clue 3: If you divide me by 2, I am an even number.

    Clue 4: My tens digit and my ones digit are the same.

3. Clue 1: I am a number between 75 and 150.

    Clue 2: My tens digit is three times my ones digit.

    Clue 3: The sum of my digits is 5.

    Clue 4: My hundreds digit and my ones digit are the same.

Rewrite the number sentences with parentheses to make them correct.

4. $204 = 7 \times 20 + 75 - 11$ **5.** $7 \times 9 - 4 = 35$

6. $42 = 3 + 3 \times 7$ **7.** $31 - 15 - 6 = 10$

8. $54 - 10 + 8 = 52$ **9.** $7 \times 8 + 3 \times 11 = 89$

10. $70 = 8 \times 8 + 6$ **11.** $3 \times 2 + 7 \times 9 = 69$

12. $98 = 7 \times 8 + 42$ **13.** $76 - 20 + 8 = 64$

Mixed Practice Set 16

In each set of problems below, do as many exercises as you can in one minute. Ask someone to time you.

Problem Set 1

1. 9×6

2. 7×7

3. $21 \div 7$

4. 12×8

5. $44 \div 4$

6. 2×10

7. 11×4

8. $64 \div 8$

9. 12×5

10. 10×11

11. $81 \div 9$

12. $54 \div 6$

13. 9×7

14. $48 \div 8$

15. 9×3

Problem Set 2

16. 12×7

17. 2×9

18. 6×6

19. 9×9

20. $121 \div 11$

21. 6×7

22. 4×12

23. $21 \div 3$

24. $108 \div 9$

25. 8×4

26. $42 \div 6$

27. $144 \div 12$

28. 4×10

29. 11×11

30. 8×3

Problem Set 3

31. 12×11

32. $54 \div 9$

33. $42 \div 7$

34. 7×3

35. 12×4

36. $55 \div 5$

37. 6×8

38. 3×11

39. $90 \div 9$

40. $48 \div 6$

41. 12×9

42. 4×7

43. 3×8

44. $132 \div 12$

45. $49 \div 7$

Mixed Practice Set 16 *(continued)*

46. The first figure is $\frac{1}{2}$ of the whole. What fraction of the whole is each of the other figures?

 a. **b.** **c.**

The fourth-grade class had a pizza party. They ordered pizzas and divided each pizza into 6 equal slices. Twenty-one students, 1 teacher, and 4 parents were invited to the party. The pupils assumed each person would eat one slice of pizza.

47. How many people were invited to the party?

48. How many slices of pizza did they need?

49. How many pizzas did the class order?

50. If everyone ate just one slice, how many slices were left over?

51. What fraction of a whole pizza is that?

52. If everyone ate two slices of pizza, how many slices did they need?

53. How many whole pizzas did the class then need?

54. What fraction of a whole pizza was left over?

55. Juana brought 3 granola bars to share equally among her and 4 of her friends. What fraction of one granola bar did each person get?

Write answers on a separate sheet of paper. Use with or after Unit 2.

Mixed Practice Set 17

Solve.

1. 212
    $\times$ 20

2. 785
    $-$ 76

3. 867
    $-$ 74

4.   900
    $+$ 1200

5.   418
        460
    $+$ 454

6.   1034
    $+$ 2349

7. 76
    $\times$ 0

8.   7210
    $+$ 9188

9.   600
    $-$ 599

10. $(60 + 80) \times 4$

11. $39 - (3 \times 4)$

12. $620 + 150 + 220$

13. $(1800 \div 60) \times 5$

14. *Use the clues to complete the place-value puzzle.*

- Write the result of $210 \div 70$ in the ten-thousands place.

- Multiply 5×7. Subtract 29. Write the result in the tens place.

- Triple the number in the ten-thousands place. Write the result in the thousands place.

- Divide 72 by 12. Add 1 and write the result in the hundreds place.

- Subtract the number in the ten-thousands place from the number in the hundreds place. Write the result in the hundred-thousands place.

- Multiply 84 by 0. Write the result in the ones place.

100,000s	10,000s	1000s	100s	10s	1s

Mixed Practice Set 18

Write a number for each picture below. Use 0 or $\frac{0}{4}$, $\frac{1}{4}$, $\frac{1}{2}$ or $\frac{2}{4}$, $\frac{3}{4}$, and 1 or $\frac{4}{4}$.

1.  **2.**  **3.**

4. 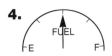 **5.**

Solve.

6. 47	**7.** 63	**8.** 214	**9.** 703
$\times\,6$	$\times\,3$	$\times\,5$	$\times\,7$

Make a name-collection box for each number listed below. Use as many different numbers and operations as you can.

Example:

419
$(\frac{1}{5} \times 2500) - (9 \times 9)$
$(205 \times 2) + 9$
$838 \div 2$
$(500 - 85) + 4$

10. 380
11. 176
12. 4218
13. 510
14. 6111
15. 495

Mixed Practice Set 18 *(continued)*

*Complete the **What's My Rule?** tables.*

16.

Rule	in	out
out = in × 12	3	36
	5	
	7	
	11	
	15	

17.

Rule	in	out
	8	24
	14	30
		44
	35	
	43	59

Solve.

18. 1800
− 927

19. 3684
− 485

20. 3164
+ 5791

21. 8261
− 3540

22. 600
− 31

23. 475
+ 250

24. 1834
+ 8365

25. 469
− 70

26. 1200
− 30

27. 2444
− 382

28. 729
+ 682

29. 1356
− 1172

30. 4321
− 1234

31. 500
− 42

32. 1300
− 485

Mixed Practice Set 19

Write the number sentences with parentheses and solve.

1. Add 5.4 to the difference of 10.5 and 7.3.

2. Subtract the sum of 9 and 3.5 from 18.75.

3. Add 19 to the difference of 25.0 and 16.4.

4. Subtract the sum of 81 and 6.2 from 848.7.

Rewrite the number sentences with parentheses to make them correct.

5. $40 \times 9 - 4 = 200$

6. $7.2 = 5.2 + 6 \div 3$

7. $330 - 150 - 6 = 186$

8. $9 - 11 + 8 = -10$

9. $7 \times 5 + 7 \times 2 = 49$

10. $310 = 40 \times 6 + 70$

11. $6 \times 3 + 9 \times 12 = 126$

12. $760 = 9.5 \times 2 + 8 \times 8$

Solve.

13. 20×80

14. 16×10

15. 82×100

16. 7×300

17. 91×10

18. 7.6×100

19. 14×200

20. 75×60

21. 400×5.0

22. 30.4×10

23. 1.9×200

24. 19×200

25. How many 7s in 1400?

26. How many 70s in 4900?

Mixed Practice Set 20

1. How many nuts are there?

2. What fraction of the nuts are peanuts?

3. What fraction of the nuts are acorns?

4. What fraction of the nuts are almonds?

5. Write the answer to Number 4 as a decimal.

Find the area, in square units, of each rectangle and then write the number model.

> **Reminder:** Area = length (l) $\times$ width (w)

Example:

Area = 16 square units
$4 \times 4 = 16$

6.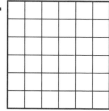

7.

8. How are all these rectangles similar?

Mixed Practice Set 20 *(continued)*

Complete the frames-and-arrows problems.

9.

Rule
+ 215

10.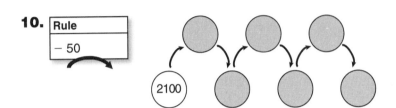

Rule
− 50

11.

Rule
÷ 4

12.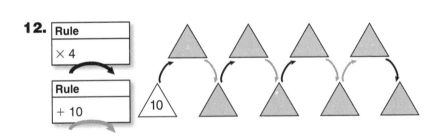

Rule
× 4

Rule
+ 10

13.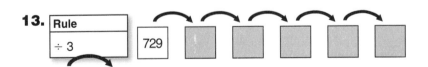

Rule
÷ 3

Mixed Practice Set 21

Write the digit in the thousandths place.

1. 5.925   **2.** 1.043   **3.** 1.100

4. 8.104   **5.** 0.280   **6.** 3.021

7. 3.313   **8.** 0.001   **9.** 10.123

Write 2 multiplication and 2 division facts for the following groups of numbers.

10. 6, 10, and 60   **11.** 2, 9, and 18

12. 4, 9, and 36   **13.** 3, 7, and 21

14. 8, 9, and 72   **15.** 5, 10, and 50

Solve.

16. $420 - \blacksquare = 81$ **17.** $712 + 517 = \blacksquare$

18. $160 + 348 = \blacksquare$ **19.** $490 - 170 = \blacksquare$

20. $2216 - 1804 = \blacksquare$ **21.** $90 = 8100 \div \blacksquare$

22. $\begin{array}{r} 387 \\ -\ 36 \\ \hline \end{array}$ **23.** $\begin{array}{r} 673 \\ -\ 615 \\ \hline \end{array}$ **24.** $\begin{array}{r} 57 \\ \times\ 7 \\ \hline \end{array}$

25. $\begin{array}{r} 7619 \\ +\ 3250 \\ \hline \end{array}$ **26.** $\begin{array}{r} 980 \\ \times\ 50 \\ \hline \end{array}$ **27.** $\begin{array}{r} 427 \\ 561 \\ +\ 711 \\ \hline \end{array}$

28. Alvin wants to wear a pair of socks for each of the 14 days he will be on vacation. How many socks does he need to pack?

Mixed Practice Set 22

Complete the frames-and-arrows problems.

1.

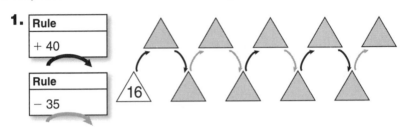

2.

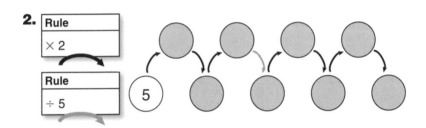

3.

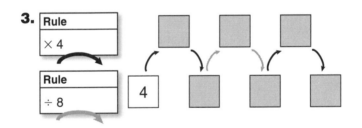

4. Write the following in digits: one hundred sixty-two thousand, nine hundred seventy-four.

5. Write the words for 171,603.

6. Write the following in digits: two hundred thousand, eight hundred forty-four.

Mixed Practice Set 22 *(continued)*

Solve.

7. $180 \div 6 = \blacksquare$

8. $24 \times 6 = \blacksquare$

9. $810 = 90 \times \blacksquare$

10. $40 \times 70 = \blacksquare$

11. $80 \times \blacksquare = 3200$

12. $\blacksquare \div 100 = 6$

13. $8400 \div 700 = \blacksquare$

14. $36 \times \blacksquare = 72$

15. $\blacksquare \div 5 = 70$

16. $9 \times 200 = \blacksquare$

17. $5400 \div \blacksquare = 9$

18. $12 \times 120 = \blacksquare$

19. How much money, without tax, will I need for 4 VCR tapes that cost $3.25 each?

20. How many dollars are in 22 five-dollar bills?

21. If 1 block is 200 meters long, how far will you run in 23 blocks?

22. There are about 8 blocks in one mile. How many blocks are in 5 miles?

23. There are 5280 feet in one mile. How many yards are in one mile? (Reminder: 1 yd = 3 ft)

24. How many five-dollar bills are in $325.00?

Mixed Practice Set 23

1. *Use the clues to complete the place-value puzzle.*

- Add 43 and 23. Divide by 11 and write the result in the ones place.

- Triple the number in the ones place and divide by 2. Write the result in the tens place.

- Multiply 8 × 9. Subtract 68. Write the result in the thousands place.

- Subtract the number in the tens place from 57 and divide by 6. Write the result in the hundred-thousands place.

- Divide 36 by the number in the thousands place. Write the result in the ten-thousands place.

- Subtract the number in the ten-thousands place from the number in the tens place. Write the result in the hundreds place.

100,000s	10,000s	1000s	100s	10s	1s

Solve.

2. 14.8 + 12.2	**3.** 113.24 + 7.56	**4.** 26 × 4	**5.** 1.80 × 7

6. 0.196 × 0	**7.** 72.1 + 19.3	**8.** 1.25 + 6.43	**9.** 12.69 − 11.41

10. 11.1 × 9	**11.** 85 − 38	**12.** 5037 + 8632	**13.** 962 − 421

Mixed Practice Set 24

Use digits to write the following numbers.

1. two hundred sixty thousand, four hundred fifty-three

2. two hundred eighty-six and thirty-eight hundredths

3. three hundred fourteen thousand, six hundred ninety-one

4. one million, seventy-four thousand, nine hundred sixty-eight

5. six million, seven hundred nine thousand, eight hundred forty-five

Write the words for the following numbers.

6. 296,069

7. 1,312,743

8. 854.09

9. 3,969,231

10. 8,201,774

*Complete the **What's My Rule?** tables.*

11.

Rule	in	out
out = in × 200	7	1400
	9	
	12	
	14	
	35	

12.

Rule	in	out
	7	$14\frac{1}{2}$
	10	$17\frac{1}{2}$
		20
	$13\frac{1}{2}$	
	$22\frac{1}{2}$	30

Mixed Practice Set 24 *(continued)*

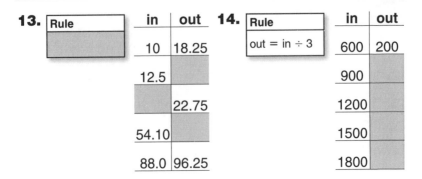

13.

Rule	in	out
	10	18.25
	12.5	
		22.75
	54.10	
	88.0	96.25

14.

Rule: out = in ÷ 3	in	out
	600	200
	900	
	1200	
	1500	
	1800	

Rewrite the number sentences with parentheses to make them correct.

15. $26 \div 2 - 7 = 6$

16. $41.2 = 7 \times 6 - 0.8$

17. $130 - 15 - 60 = 55$

18. $118 = 2 \times 55.7 + 3.3$

19. $10 \times 2.1 + 5 \times 12.2 = 82$

20. $30 = 6 \times 20 - 90$

21. $11 \times 12 + 7 - 4 = 165$

22. $99 = 11 \times 50 - 41$

23. $50 + 300 \div 5 = 70$

24. $200 \times 2.6 - 1.1 + 5 = 305$

Write answers on a separate sheet of paper.　　　　Use with or after Unit 3.

Mixed Practice Set 25

1. What is the temperature difference, in °C, between Body Temperature and Room Temperature?

2. What is the temperature difference, in °F, between the boiling point and freezing point for water?

3. What is the temperature difference, in °F, between the freezing point for water and the freezing point for a salt solution? What is the difference in °C?

4. How much colder is −110°F than 7°F?

5. How much warmer is 42°C than −18°C?

6. Which is colder, −32°C or −32°F?

7. Which is warmer, 48°C or 108°F?

8. Imagine it is 22°C outside. Which would be a better activity: ice skating or bike riding?

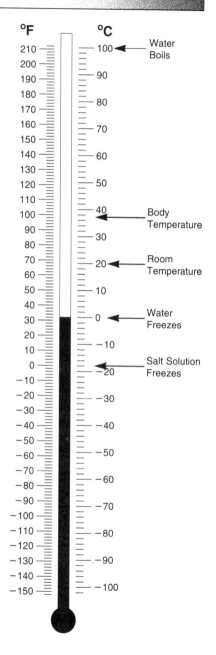

Mixed Practice Set 25 *(continued)*

Table of Equivalents		
3 * 4	12/3	12 ÷ 3
3 × 4	$\frac{12}{3}$	3)12

Write two multiplication and two division facts for each of the following fact triangles:

9.
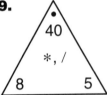

10.
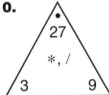

Solve.

11. You went to the store with a $10 bill and a $5 bill. Your groceries cost $12.36. How much change should you get?

12. $\frac{20}{4}$ **13.** $\frac{36}{9}$ **14.** 7 * 7   **15.** 6 * 6

16. 9 * 80   **17.** 12 + 13   **18.** 41 − 25   **19.** 7 * 8

20. 5 * 6   **21.** $\frac{12}{12}$ **22.** $\frac{40}{10}$ **23.** $\frac{48}{6}$

Use digits to write the following numbers:

24. forty-five thousand, three hundred ninety-two

25. four hundred fifty-nine thousand, seven hundred three

Mixed Practice Set 26

Make a name-collection box for each number listed below. Use as many different numbers and operations as you can.

Example:

24
XXIV
$48 \div 2$
$29 - 5$
12×2

1. 15
2. 100
3. 54
4. 73

True or False?

Example: $12 + 15 = 25$ *(False)*
        $4 \times (3 + 1) = 16$ *(True)*

5. $7 \times 9 = 54$ **6.** $3 * (4 + 5) = 27$

7. $5 * 6 = 40$ **8.** $(99 + 13) = 103$

---

9. *Use the clues to complete the place-value puzzle.*

- Divide 18 by 6. Write the result in the ones place.
- Double the number in the ones place. Divide by 3. Write the result in the tens place.
- Write the result of 8×5 divided by 10 in the thousands place.
- Multiply 7 by 2. Subtract 7. Write the result in the hundreds place.

1000s	100s	10s	1s

Mixed Practice Set 26 (continued)

Solve.

10. 23 × 4 **11.** 18 ÷ 1 **12.** 54 + 36

13. 9 * 35 **14.** 180 / 10 **15.** 78 − 23

16. 50 × 60 **17.** 162 / 6 **18.** 48 − 12

Examine the data sets. Find the mean of each.

Example: 7 6 5 9 8

Step 1 Find the total of the numbers in the data set.

$$7 + 6 + 5 + 9 + 8 = 35$$

Step 2 Count how many numbers are in the data set.
There are 5 numbers in all.

Step 3 Divide the total by the amount of numbers.

$$\frac{35}{5} = 7 \qquad \text{Mean} = 7$$

19. 5 8 8 11 7 9 **20.** 12 10 8 14 11

21. 3 2 3 1 6 4 2 **22.** 14 15 18 13

Write the missing numbers.

23.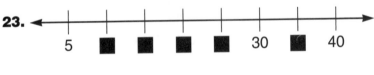

24.

Write answers on a separate sheet of paper. Use with or after Unit 4.

Mixed Practice Set 27

Complete the number models.

1. $(4 \times 8) - 6 = \blacksquare$

2. $4 * (8 - 6) = \blacksquare$

3. $(16 + 27) - 8 = \blacksquare$

4. $16 + (27 - 8) = \blacksquare$

5. $(36 - 12) - 5 = \blacksquare$

6. $36 - (12 - 5) = \blacksquare$

7. $\blacksquare = (18 / 3) + 6$

8. $\blacksquare = 18 \div (3 + 6)$

9. $\blacksquare = (7 + 4) \times (3 - 1)$

10. $\blacksquare = 7 + (4 \times 3) - 1$

11. $\blacksquare = (50 \div 5) \div 5$

12. $\blacksquare = 50 / (5 / 5)$

Use the statements below to help you solve the problems.

- The average person throws away about 5 pounds of trash per day.
- One ton is equal to 2000 pounds.
- There are about 250 million people in the United States.

13. How much trash does the average person throw away in one week?

14. How much trash does the average person throw away in one year?

15. About how many tons is that?

16. About how many tons of trash does the average family of 4 throw away in one year?

17. Does the population of the United States produce more or less than 10 million tons of trash per year?

18. About how many tons of trash does the United States produce in one year?

Mixed Practice Set 28

Solve.

1. 20 ÷ 4   **2.** 36 / 9   **3.** 12 ÷ 12   **4.** 40 ÷ 10

5. 48 ÷ 6   **6.** 8 / 4   **7.** 0 / 4   **8.** 18 ÷ 1

9. 12 ÷ 4   **10.** 24 / 8   **11.** 4 ÷ 8   **12.** 144 ÷ 12

Solve.

13.　35
　　　× 4

14.　62
　　　× 3

15.　265
　　　× 8

16.　4354
　　　+ 1897

17.　7108
　　　+ 1362

18.　500
　　　+ 4500

19.　3249
　　　− 1933

20.　1865
　　　− 674

Write the missing numbers.

21.

Rule
∗ 3

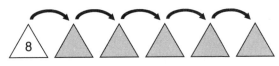

22.

Rule
∗ 4

Rule
− 8

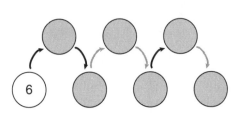

Write answers on a separate sheet of paper.　　　　　Use with or after Unit 4.

23.

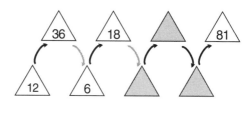

Rule

Rule

---

24. *Use the clues to complete the place-value puzzle.*

- Divide 60 by 12. Write the result in the ones place.

- Triple the number in the ones place and divide by 3. Write the result in the hundreds place.

- 4 is the square of ■. Write the result in the millions place.

- Halve the number in the millions place. Multiply by 6 and write the result in the thousands place.

- Multiply 3 by itself. Write the result in the tens place.

- Subtract the number in the ones place from the number in the thousands place. Write the result in the hundred-thousands place.

- Divide 42 by the number in the thousands place. Write the result in the ten-thousands place.

1,000,000s	100,000s	10,000s	1000s	100s	10s	1s

Mixed Practice Set 29

Solve.

1. Two regular-size paper clips weigh about 1 gram. About how many paper clips would it take to weigh 10 grams?

2. About how many clips would it take to weigh 1 kilogram? (One kilogram = 1000 grams.)

3. One ounce is about 30 grams. About how many regular-size paper clips are there in 1 ounce?

4. How many clips are there in 1 pound?

5. About how much does a box of 1000 paper clips weigh if the empty box weighs 15 grams?

6.	374	7.	1594	8.	18	9.	160
	+ 735		+ 2629		× 5		× 4

10.	768	11.	12.93	12.	3.9	13.	7.70
	− 147		+ 28.16		+ 6.4		+ 5.42

14.	1.64	15.	412	16.	6731	17.	6473
	× 0		− 37		+ 327		− 5269

Solve.

18. 8 * 9   19. 96 / 8

20. 60 ÷ 12   21. 12 × 7

22. 6 × 11   23. 9 * 5

24. 6 × 4   25. 80 / 10

26. 10 * 11   27. 7 × 11

Write answers on a separate sheet of paper.   Use with or after Unit 4.

Mixed Practice Set 30

Solve the following questions. (The prices include tax.)

Shoelaces	Construction Paper	Toothbrush
1 pair	1 pad	soft-bristle
$1.08	$0.89	$0.89

Gift Wrap	Audio Tape	Greeting Cards
5 sq ft roll	60 minutes	box of 12
$1.85	$1.67	$4.20

1. Tom is going shopping. Each of his two children needs a pair of shoelaces, a toothbrush, and a pad of construction paper. Estimate to the nearest dollar how much money he will need.

2. Briana needs enough wrapping paper to cover her five presents. She has 6 dollars and she estimates that she will need three rolls. Does she have enough money? What is the difference between the amount of money she has and the amount she needs?

3. Joe and Ahmed are researching the 50-year history of their school. They need to buy enough audio tapes for an hour-and-a-half interview with the principal. How much money do they need?

4. How much money does each of the greeting cards in the box of 12 cost?

Mixed Practice Set 30 *(continued)*

Solve.

5. $3.40 * 5 = \blacksquare$

6. $36 = 6 \times \blacksquare$

7. $8.27 + 4.31 = \blacksquare$

8. $6 \times \blacksquare = \$1.80$

9. $\blacksquare \div 150 = 5$

10. $14.0 - 9.2 = \blacksquare$

11. $22 \times \blacksquare = 66$

12. $280 \div \blacksquare = 7$

Make a name-collection box for each number listed below. Use as many different numbers and operations as you can.

Example:

43.12
$43 + 0.12$
$86.24 \div 2$
$50 - 6.88$
$(6 * 7) + (2 * 0.56)$

13. 92.47

14. 49.16

15. 345.63

Estimate the total cost.

16. 16 pencils that cost 7¢ each

17. 8 scissors that cost $0.75 each

18. 2 books that cost $8.57 each

19. 12 rulers that cost $1.08 each

20. 3 pairs of shoes that cost $26.95 each

Write answers on a separate sheet of paper.   Use with or after Unit 4.

Mixed Practice Set 31

1. How many pieces of fruit are there?

2. What fraction of the fruit are apples?

3. What fraction of the fruit are pears?

4. What fraction of the fruit are bananas?

5. What fraction of the fruit are oranges?

Complete the frames-and-arrows problem.

6.

Rule
+ 20 min

1:55

Find the missing factors.

7. 8 * ■ = 24

8. ■ * 90 = 360

9. ■ * 7 = 49

10. 2 * ■ = 960

11. 60 * ■ = 3600

12. ■ * 7 = 350

13. 8 * ■ = 640

14. ■ * 32 = 640

Mixed Practice Set 32

Who am I?

1. Clue 1: I am less than 10.
Clue 2: I am an even number.
Clue 3: I am a square number.

2. Clue 1: I am less than 100.
Clue 2: The sum of my digits is 17.
Clue 3: I am an even number.

3. Clue 1: I am a number between 100 and 200.
Clue 2: The sum of my digits is 3.
Clue 3: My ones digit is two times my hundreds digit.

4. The first figure is $\frac{3}{4}$ of the whole. What fraction of the whole is each of the other figures?

 a. **b.** **c.**

5. Write a number for each picture. Use 0 or $\frac{0}{4}$, $\frac{1}{4}$, $\frac{1}{2}$, $\frac{3}{4}$, and $\frac{4}{4}$ or 1.

a. **b.**

c. **d.** **e.**

Write answers on a separate sheet of paper.   Use with or after Unit 5.

Mixed Practice Set 32 *(continued)*

Solve.

6. 326
  $\times\, 30$

7. 965
  $-\, 86$

8. 541
  $-\, 8$

9.   160
  $+\, 1400$

10. 6045
  $+\, 248$

11.   2289
  $+\, 1374$

12.   18
  $\times\, 11$

13.   4371
  $+\, 8148$

14. 890
  $-\, 15$

15. $(70 + 15) * 4$

16. $67 - (8 * 4)$

17. $430 + 70 + 145$

18. $(72 / 8) * 3$

19. Alice records her weight change every week. For the past three weeks she recorded +3, −1, and +2 pounds. Can you tell how much she weighs?

Rewrite the number sentences with parentheses to make them correct.

20. $412 = 70 * 5 + 1 - 8$

21. $6 * 10 - 5 = 55$

22. $81 = 7 + 2 * 9$

23. $39 - 16 - 4 = 19$

24. $44 - 13 + 23 = 8$

25. $8 * 5 + 2 * 18 = 76$

26. $135 = 9 * 9 + 6$

27. $4 * 3 + 7 * 6 = 240$

Mixed Practice Set 33

1. *Use the clues to complete the place-value puzzle.*

- Write the result of 36 − 28 in the thousands place.

- Multiply 6 × 3 and subtract 17. Write the result in the ones place.

- Triple the number in the thousands place and divide by 4. Write the result in the hundreds place.

- Subtract 3 from the result of 270 divided by 90. Write the result in the ten-thousands place.

- Divide 135 by 27. Write the result in the hundred-thousands place.

- Subtract the number in the hundred-thousands place from the number in the thousands place. Write the result in the tens place.

100,000s	10,000s	1000s	100s	10s	1s

*Complete the **What's My Rule?** tables.*

2.

Rule	in	out
out = in ∗ 22	3	66
	4	
	8	
	14	
	16	

3.

Rule	in	out
	12	132
	13	143
		154
	18	
	20	220

Mixed Practice Set 34

1. Eight people are going to share $168 equally.
  a. How many $10 bills does each person get?
  b. How many dollars are left to share?
  c. From the money that remains, how many $1 bills does each person get?
  d. What is the total number of dollars each person gets?
  e. Write a number model for this problem.

2. Five people are going to share $1025 equally.
  a. How many $100 bills does each person get?
  b. From the money that remains, how many $10 bills does each person get?
  c. How many dollars are left to share?
  d. From the money that remains, how many $1 bills does each person get?
  e. What is the total number of dollars each person gets?
  f. Write a number model for this problem.

3. Three people are going to share $817.50 equally.
  a. How many $100 bills does each person get?
  b. From the money that remains, how many $10 bills does each person get?
  c. How many dollars are left to share?
  d. From the money that remains, how many $1 bills does each person get?
  e. How much money is left over?
  f. If the leftover money is shared equally, how many cents does each person get?
  g. Write a number model for this problem.

4.	352	**5.**	118	**6.**	3276	**7.**	768
	− 247		× 7		+ 1398		− 89

8. 5472
  − 3719

9. 30)180

10. 7)168

11. 9)144

12. 408
  323
  + 475

13. 205
  335
  + 182

14. 382
  416
  + 249

15. 414
  627
  + 100

Write the amounts.

16. (Q)(Q)(Q)(Q)(Q)(D)(D)(N)(N)(P)(P)(P)

17. $1 | $1 | $1 (Q)(D)(D)(D)(D)(P)(P)

18. $5 | $5 | $5 | $5 | $5 | $1
  (Q)(N)(N)

19. $100 | $100 | $20 | $20 | $5 | $1 | $1

Write the missing numbers.

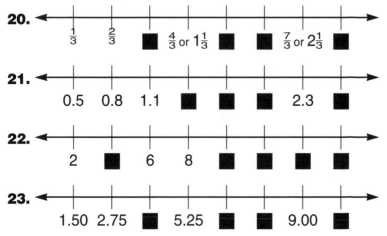

20. $\frac{1}{3}$ $\frac{2}{3}$ ■ $\frac{4}{3}$ or $1\frac{1}{3}$ ■ ■ $\frac{7}{3}$ or $2\frac{1}{3}$ ■

21. 0.5 0.8 1.1 ■ ■ ■ 2.3 ■

22. 2 ■ 6 8 ■ ■ ■ ■

23. 1.50 2.75 ■ 5.25 ■ ■ 9.00 ■

Mixed Practice Set 35

In each set of problems below, do as many exercises as you can in one minute. Ask someone to time you.

Problem Set 1

1. $12 - 6 = \blacksquare$

2. $16 \div 4 = \blacksquare$

3. $8 * \blacksquare = 40$

4. $54 / 9 = \blacksquare$

5. $5 + 3 = \blacksquare$

6. $11 - 8 = \blacksquare$

7. $100 \div 10 = \blacksquare$

8. $\blacksquare * 9 = 36$

9. $12 \times 6 = \blacksquare$

10. $3 * \blacksquare = 27$

11. $4 + 7 = \blacksquare$

12. $20 / 5 = \blacksquare$

13. $15 - 8 = \blacksquare$

14. $6 + 9 = \blacksquare$

15. $36 \div \blacksquare = 6$

Problem Set 2

16. $9 + 2 = \blacksquare$

17. $32 / 8 = \blacksquare$

18. $5 * \blacksquare = 25$

19 $30 \div 5 = \blacksquare$

20. $6 + \blacksquare = 14$

21. $10 - 7 = \blacksquare$

22. $64 \div 8 = \blacksquare$

23. $\blacksquare \times 7 = 56$

24. $4 * 6 = \blacksquare$

25. $4 \times \blacksquare = 48$

26. $16 - 7 = \blacksquare$

27. $45 \div 5 = \blacksquare$

28. $16 / 4 = \blacksquare$

29. $12 - \blacksquare = 6$

30. $7 + 6 = \blacksquare$

Solve.

31. If you flipped a coin 10 times, how many times would you expect to get heads? Try it. Record the result as a fraction and as a percent. Do the experiment and record the result again. How similar were your results and your prediction?

Mixed Practice Set 36

Complete the **What's My Rule?** tables.

1.

Rule: out = in * 25	in	out
	3	
	4	
	8	
		350
	16	

2.

Rule: out = in / 9	in	out
	81	
	54	
		12
	117	
		7

Solve.

3. $207 - \blacksquare = 65$

4. $521 + 227 = \blacksquare$

5. $190 + 448 = \blacksquare$

6. $690 - 237 = \blacksquare$

7. $1416 - 948 = \blacksquare$

8. $60 = 5400 \div \blacksquare$

9.
$$\begin{array}{r} 869 \\ -\ 44 \\ \hline \end{array}$$

10.
$$\begin{array}{r} 483 \\ -\ 355 \\ \hline \end{array}$$

11.
$$\begin{array}{r} 68 \\ \times\ 8 \\ \hline \end{array}$$

12.
$$\begin{array}{r} 8521 \\ +\ 4349 \\ \hline \end{array}$$

13.
$$\begin{array}{r} 1050 \\ \times\ 4 \\ \hline \end{array}$$

14.
$$\begin{array}{r} 2756 \\ +\ 1711 \\ \hline \end{array}$$

Mixed Practice Set 36 *(continued)*

WEIGHT NOT TO EXCEED	Ground Service ZONES						
	2	**3**	**4**	**5**	**6**	**7**	**8**
1 lb	$ 2.53	$ 2.67	$ 2.87	$ 2.95	$ 3.03	$ 3.10	$ 3.16
2	2.55	2.69	3.12	3.21	3.40	3.50	3.72
3	2.64	2.85	3.29	3.43	3.67	3.84	4.13
4	2.73	2.98	3.41	3.59	3.86	4.07	4.45
5	2.83	3.09	3.48	3.66	4.01	4.24	4.66
6	2.93	3.17	3.53	3.71	4.11	4.41	4.81
7	3.03	3.23	3.58	3.76	4.21	4.58	5.05
8	3.13	3.28	3.63	3.82	4.34	4.83	5.42
9	3.22	3.36	3.68	3.91	4.53	5.15	5.83
10	3.31	3.44	3.73	4.08	4.76	5.48	6.20
11	3.39	3.53	3.81	4.31	5.02	5.83	6.65
12	3.47	3.63	3.92	4.52	5.34	6.18	7.08
13	3.54	3.74	4.09	4.74	5.63	6.56	7.52
14	3.61	3.86	4.27	4.96	5.92	6.91	7.96
15	3.68	4.00	4.45	5.19	6.20	7.28	8.40

* FOR ANY FRACTION OF A POUND OVER THE WEIGHT
SHOWN, USE THE NEXT HIGHER RATE.

Use the chart above to answer the questions.

15. You want to ship a package to your uncle, who lives in Zone 3. The package weighs 8 pounds 2 ounces. How much does it cost to ship your package?

16. Joan paid $4.96 to ship a package to Zone 5. What is the maximum weight the package could have weighed?

17. Walter sent two packages to Zone 7. One weighed 6 pounds and one weighed 5 pounds. How much could he have saved if he had sent them together as one package?

18. How much less is it to ship a package to Zone 2 than to Zone 3 if the package weighs $9\frac{1}{2}$ pounds?

19. Tori sent her brother a 15-pound package. She paid about twice as much as if she had sent it to Zone 2. To what zone did she send the package?

Mixed Practice Set 37

Solve.

1. 16×24

2. $91 - 35$

3. 31×42

4. $7\overline{)42}$

5. $486 \div 18$

6. $16\overline{)336}$

7. $185 - 78$

8. $748 + 546$

9. 87×12

10. $496 / 8$

11. 79×57

12. $9017 + 4526$

13. Daniel planted 6 rows of beets in his garden, with 24 beets in each row. How many beets did he plant in all?

14. The tank of Mr. Washington's car holds about 16 gallons of gasoline. About how many gallons are in the tank when the gauge shows $\frac{1}{2}$ full?

15. When the gas tank is about $\frac{1}{4}$ full, Mr. Washington stops to fill the tank. If gasoline costs $1.50 per gallon, about how much does it cost to fill the tank?

16. Joshua records his weight change every week. At the beginning of March, he weighed 87 pounds. His weekly weight fluctuations in March were +2, −1, +1 and +3 pounds. What was Joshua's total weight change for March? How much did he weigh at the end of the month?

Mixed Practice Set 37 *(continued)*

Use digits to write the following numbers.

17. two million, seven hundred eighteen thousand, nine hundred twenty

18. seven hundred sixty-nine thousand, two hundred thirty-one

19. eighteen and nine hundred seventy-eight thousandths

Write the words for the following numbers.

20. 18,564,290   **21.** 48.128

22. 5,773,963   **23.** 102,756

Write the amounts.

24. | $1 | Q Q Q Q Q Q Q D P
P P P

25. | $5 | $1 | $1 | Q Q Q N N N N

26. | $100 | $20 | $5 | $5 | $5 | $1 | $1 |

27. Q Q Q Q Q Q D N N N P P

Mixed Practice Set 38

Solve.

1. $\begin{array}{r} 26 \\ \times\ 30 \\ \hline \end{array}$ **2.** $\begin{array}{r} 70 \\ \times\ 18 \\ \hline \end{array}$ **3.** $\begin{array}{r} 94 \\ \times\ 18 \\ \hline \end{array}$ **4.** $\begin{array}{r} 40 \\ \times\ 88 \\ \hline \end{array}$

5. $\begin{array}{r} 3819 \\ -\ 2758 \\ \hline \end{array}$ **6.** $\begin{array}{r} 50 \\ \times\ 17 \\ \hline \end{array}$ **7.** $\begin{array}{r} 297 \\ +\ 4612 \\ \hline \end{array}$ **8.** $\begin{array}{r} 38 \\ \times\ 20 \\ \hline \end{array}$

9. $\begin{array}{r} 8918 \\ -\ 84 \\ \hline \end{array}$ **10.** $\begin{array}{r} 80 \\ \times\ 46 \\ \hline \end{array}$ **11.** $\begin{array}{r} 30 \\ \times\ 75 \\ \hline \end{array}$ **12.** $\begin{array}{r} 90 \\ \times\ 62 \\ \hline \end{array}$

13. Steve's room measures 12 by 13 feet. He wants to lay down new carpeting on his floor. How many square feet does he need to buy?

Make a name-collection box for each of the numbers below. Use as many different numbers and operations as you can.

Example:

1.986
10×0.1986
$\frac{1986}{1000}$
$6 - 4.014$
$3.972 / 2$

14. 49.167
15. 5.635
16. 201.386

Mixed Practice Set 38 *(continued)*

The residents of an apartment building were asked how many people live in their households. The tallies in the table show the results of the survey. Use the table to help you answer the questions below.

17. How many households were interviewed?

18. How many people live in the building?

19. What is the median number of people per household in the building?

20. What is the approximate mean number (average) of people per household in the building?

People per household	Number of households
1	///
2	////
3	//// //
4	//// /
5	//
6	//

Complete the frames-and-arrows problems.

21.

Rule
+ 45 min

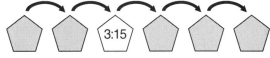

22.

Rule
+ 10¢

Rule
− $1.80

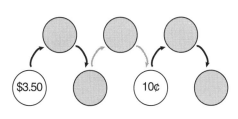

Mixed Practice Set 39

Who am I?

1. Clue 1: I am less than 20.
Clue 2: I am an odd number.
Clue 3: I am the square root of 225.

2. Clue 1: I am less than 100.
Clue 2: I am an even number.
Clue 3: I can be represented by an array of
7 rows and 8 columns.

3. Clue 1: I am less than 1000.
Clue 2: The sum of my digits is 26.
Clue 3: My ones digit is eight.

---

*Write two multiplication and two division problems for
each of the following triangles:*

4.
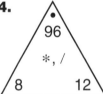

5.
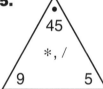

6.
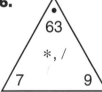

7.
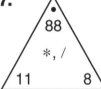

8.
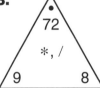

9.
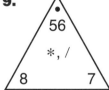

Write answers on a separate sheet of paper.   Use with or after Unit 6.

Mixed Practice Set 40

Solve. (Prices include tax.)

$3.99

$1.99

$1.59

1. Ms. Jackson wants to buy enough crayons to give 1 to each of her 29 students. She has $3.50.

   a. What can she buy?

   b. How many crayons will she have left over?

2. How many boxes of 16 crayons would it take to equal the number in the 64-crayon box?

3. How much would this cost?

4. Estimate whether $18 is enough to buy 5 boxes of 64 crayons.

Solve.

5. 29 ∗ 3

6. 57 ∗ 8

7. 495 ∗ 6

8. 307 × 4

9. 860 × 7

10. 334 ∗ 11

11. Draw an array that represents the number model 4 ∗ 7 = 28

Mixed Practice Set 40 *(continued)*

12. Which temperature is colder, −7°C or −6°C?

13. Which is warmer, +2°C or −13°C?

Find the volume of each rectangular prism.

Volume = length × width × height
= area of base × height

1 cubic unit

14.

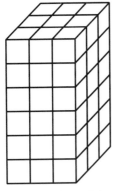

Volume = ___ cubic units

15.

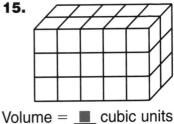

Volume = ___ cubic units

16.

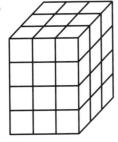

Volume = ___ cubic units

17.

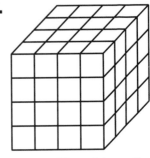

Volume = ___ cubic units

Mixed Practice Set 41

Solve.

1. 56
    + 98

2. 13
    + 73

3. 74
    − 46

4. 30
    − 19

5. 623
    351
  + 249

6. 403
    + 382

7. 91
   × 100

8. 5348
    + 6155

9. 4390
    − 240

10. (80 + 80) * 5

11. 36 − (7 * 9)

12. 60 + 450 + 338

13. (40 * 5) − 30

14. A dragonfly measures about 68 mm long, while a horsefly measures about 23 mm. How much larger is the dragonfly than the horsefly?

Write two equivalent fractions for the following numbers.

15. $\frac{1}{3}$

16. $\frac{3}{4}$

17. $\frac{3}{6}$

18. $\frac{5}{12}$

19. $\frac{10}{16}$

20. $\frac{14}{7}$

21. 1

22. $\frac{6}{9}$

Mixed Practice Set 41 *(continued)*

23. *Put these numbers in order from smallest to largest.*

14,001   114,000   110.41   41,000

Write the next three numbers in each pattern.

24. 4, 8, 16   **25.** 85, 90, 95

26. 16, 12, 8   **27.** 2, 0, –2

---

28. *Use the clues to complete the place-value puzzle.*

- Add 3 to the result of 71 – 68. Write the result in the hundredths place.
- Write the result of 54 / 9 in the ones place.
- Multiply 6 * 12. Subtract 65. Write the result in the tens place.
- Double the number in the ones place. Then divide by 3 and write the result in the thousandths place.
- Divide 24 by 6. Add 5 and write the result in the tenths place.

10s	1s	.	0.1s	0.01s	0.001s

Make a name-collection box for each number below. Use as many different numbers and operations as you can.

Example:

0.12
0.1 + 0.02
2 × 0.06
$\frac{12}{100}$

29. 2.5

30. 0.40

31. 0.68

Mixed Practice Set 42

1. What time does the clock show? Write your answer to the nearest minute.

2. What time will it be in 50 minutes?

3. What time will it be in 128 minutes?

4. What time was it 2 hours and 25 minutes ago?

---

*Complete the **What's My Rule?** tables.*

5.

Rule	in	out
out = in + 15	18	
	34	
		56
	48	
	90	

6.

Rule	in	out
out = in − 22	43	
	34	
		9
	18	
		77

7.

Rule	in	out
out = in * 4	0	
		8
	4	
	10	
	15	

8.

Rule	in	out
out = in / 3	18	
		12
	60	
		30
		40

Mixed Practice Set 43

1. *Write the number that has*

4 in the tens place

7 in the hundred-thousands place

5 in the ones place

0 in the thousands place

6 in the hundreds place

8 in the ten-thousands place

Judy brought 12 quarters to the arcade. She spent $\frac{1}{3}$ of them on video games and $\frac{1}{2}$ on basketball.

2. How much did she spend on video games?

3. How much did she spend on basketball?

4. How much money was left?

5. What fraction of the total is that?

6. Write two equivalent fractions for your answer.

Mixed Practice Set 44

Solve.

1. 125
   $+ 76$

2. 43
   $\times 4$

3. 610
   $\times 8$

4. 810
   $- 271$

5. 680
   $- 596$

6. 47
   $+ 72$

7. 1015
   $- 450$

8. 600
   $- 310$

9. 204
   $+ 329$

10. 8134
   $+ 3538$

11. 2000
   $- 199$

12. 460
   $- 280$

13. It takes Sam about 35 minutes to get ready for school. If the bus comes by at 7:45 A.M., what time should Sam get up?

14. 6 * ■ = 18

15. 3 * 7 = ■

16. 16 / 4 = ■

17. 20 / ■ = 4

18. 24 / 8 = ■

19. 9 * 4 = ■

20. 8 * ■ = 64

21. 81 = ■ × 9

22. 2 × 30 = ■

23. 540 ÷ ■ = 90

Mixed Practice Set 44 *(continued)*

Complete the frames-and-arrows problems.

24.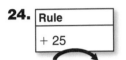

25.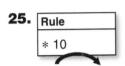

26.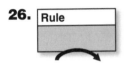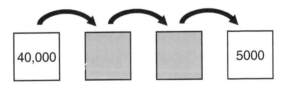

27.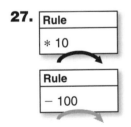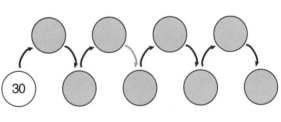

Mixed Practice Set 45

Write the number sentences with parentheses and solve.

1. Add 25 to the difference of 115 and 63.

2. Subtract the sum of 18 and 32 from 158.

3. Add 19 to the difference of 150 and 116.

4. Subtract the sum of 58 and 42 from 210.

Rewrite the number sentences with parentheses to make them correct.

5. $7 * 9 - 4 = 59$

6. $19 = 7 + 4 \times 3$

7. $31 - 14 - 5 = 12$

8. $55 - 12 + 9 = 34$

9. $4 \times 9 + 4 \times 12 = 84$

10. $44 = 4 \times 7 + 4$

11. $9 * 1 + 7 * 8 = 576$

12. $6 * 10 + 14 = 74$

Solve.

13. How many 25s in 300?

14. How many 50s in 1200?

15. 8×2000

16. 2500×3

17. 1500×7

18. 3300×30

19. Without measuring, estimate this line segment to the nearest centimeter.

Mixed Practice Set 46

Answer the questions by writing each fraction in simplest terms.

1. What fraction of the coins are pennies?

2. What fraction of the coins are nickels?

3. What fraction of the coins are dimes?

4. How much money is there in the whole group?

5. If you took away $\frac{1}{3}$ of the dimes, how much money would be left?

Write the digit in the hundredths place for each of the following.

6. 0.108   **7.** 13.313   **8.** 5.925   **9.** 4.078

Write 2 multiplication and 2 division facts for the following groups of numbers.

10. 4, 9, and 36   **11.** 6, 8, and 48

12. 10, 7, and 70   **13.** 7, 6, and 42

Solve.

14. $82 + 17 = \blacksquare$ **15.** $70 + 26 = \blacksquare$

16. $40 - 17 = \blacksquare$ **17.** $16 - 8 = \blacksquare$

18. $9 * 9 = \blacksquare$ **19.** $120 - \blacksquare = 30$

20. 332
      − 140

21. 38
      × 8

22. 1294
      + 5729

23. 600
      × 50

24. 702
      125
      + 311

25. 39
      + 67

26. 44
      + 35

27. 92
      − 48

28. 50
      − 16

29. 87
      − 36

30. 73
      − 58

31. 509
      − 376

Use the following list of numbers to answer the questions.

18, 6, 7, 9, 11, 4, 14, 8, 11, 3, 6, 11

32. Which number is the smallest?

33. Which number is the largest?

34. What is the difference between the smallest and largest numbers?

35. Which number appears most often?

Complete the frames-and-arrows problem.

36.

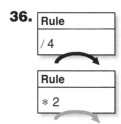 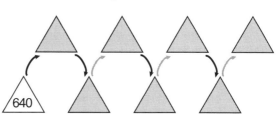

Mixed Practice Set 47

For each Fact Minute below, do as many problems as you can in that minute.

Fact Minute 1	Fact Minute 2	Fact Minute 3
1. 9 × 6	**16.** 4 * 8	**31.** 18 / 6
2. 2 * 8	**17.** 24 / 4	**32.** 7 × 7
3. 4 × 5	**18.** 5 * 9	**33.** 54 / 9
4. 8 * 4	**19.** 2 × 7	**34.** 64 / 8
5. 3 * 8	**20.** 3 × 4	**35.** 20 / 5
6. 8 × 7	**21.** 27 / 3	**36.** 9 * 5
7. 49 / 7	**22.** 6 × 8	**37.** 7 * 4
8. 7 × 5	**23.** 6 * 6	**38.** 28 / 7
9. 8 / 4	**24.** 2 * 6	**39.** 48 / 8
10. 6 * 2	**25.** 3 × 6	**40.** 32 / 4
11. 45 / 9	**26.** 7 * 3	**41.** 9 * 7
12. 32 / 8	**27.** 9 * 9	**42.** 8 * 4
13. 2 * 5	**28.** 63 / 9	**43.** 9 * 5
14. 9 * 8	**29.** 72 / 8	**44.** 72 / 9
15. 6 * 3	**30.** 81 / 9	**45.** 48 / 6

Mixed Practice Set 48

Write the next three numbers in each pattern.

1. 36, 33, 30, **2.** 10, 25, 40,

3. 48, 42, 36, **4.** 40, 5, –30,

---

5. *Order these numbers from largest to smallest.*

3200 32,000 2300 23,000

Solve.

6. ■ / 70 = 70 **7.** 6 * 30 = ■

8. 4500 / ■ = 5 **9.** 9 * 90 = ■

10. 80 / 8 = ■ **11.** 30 * 80 = ■

12. ■ / 1000 = 8 **13.** 1400 / 700 = ■

14. 28 * ■ = 560 **15.** 800 = 8 * ■

16. 4 * 400 = ■ **17.** 30 * ■ = 1500

Write numbers for the fractional parts shown in each picture.

18.  **19.**

20.  **21.**

Write as dollars and cents.

22. 18 dimes **23.** 13 quarters **24.** 35 nickels

25. 20 quarters and 6 dimes

26. Add the four amounts together.

Solve.

27. 3389
      + 1974

28. 2974
      + 189

29. 26
       × 4

30. 45
       × 7

31.   40
      × 500

32. 1.23
      + 7.91

33. 4.6
      + 4.9

34. 11.40
       − 6.83

35. 12
       × 9

36. 58
       − 22

37. 205
       832
      + 117

38. 8362
      − 4170

39. *Use the clues to complete the place-value puzzle.*

- Divide 72 by 9. Subtract 4 and write the result in the ones place.

- Double the number in the ones place. Write the result in the hundreds place.

- Multiply 8 * 10. Subtract 75. Write the result in the hundred-thousands place.

- Halve the number in the ones place. Multiply by 3 and write the result in the millions place.

- Divide 28 by the number in the ones place. Write the result in the ten-thousands place.

- Write the digit 1 in the remaining places.

1,000,000s	100,000s	10,000s	1000s	100s	10s	1s

Mixed Practice Set 49

For each Fact Minute below, do as many problems as you can in that minute.

Fact Minute 1	Fact Minute 2	Fact Minute 3
1. $13 - 4$	**16.** $4 - 0$	**31.** $12 - 9$
2. $13 - 8$	**17.** $14 - 7$	**32.** $11 - 6$
3. $12 - 7$	**18.** $9 - 9$	**33.** $10 - 7$
4. $14 - 5$	**19.** $18 - 9$	**34.** $16 - 8$
5. $17 - 9$	**20.** $10 - 1$	**35.** $11 - 4$
6. $12 - 8$	**21.** $15 - 7$	**36.** $11 - 5$
7. $12 - 4$	**22.** $13 - 7$	**37.** $10 - 2$
8. $14 - 8$	**23.** $13 - 5$	**38.** $15 - 9$
9. $12 - 3$	**24.** $10 - 6$	**39.** $12 - 6$
10. $16 - 9$	**25.** $19 - 8$	**40.** $11 - 3$
11. $15 - 8$	**26.** $12 - 5$	**41.** $14 - 9$
12. $15 - 6$	**27.** $13 - 9$	**42.** $14 - 6$
13. $10 - 3$	**28.** $13 - 6$	**43.** $16 - 7$
14. $11 - 8$	**29.** $17 - 8$	**44.** $11 - 2$
15. $9 - 5$	**30.** $11 - 7$	**45.** $10 - 4$

Mixed Practice Set 50

1. Without measuring, estimate the length of this line segment to the nearest inch

2. Make 100s.

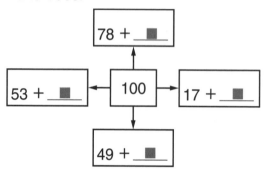

3. A square number is the product of a number multiplied by itself. For example, 25 is a square number because 5 * 5 = 25. Which of the following numbers are square numbers?

16   28   36   100   54

Write two equivalent fractions for the following numbers.

4. $\frac{1}{6}$ **5.** $\frac{3}{7}$

6. $\frac{3}{9}$ **7.** $\frac{6}{8}$

8. $\frac{11}{14}$ **9.** $\frac{3}{5}$

10. $\frac{4}{4}$ **11.** $\frac{12}{20}$

Mixed Practice Set 50 *(continued)*

In each set of problems below, do as many exercises as you can in one minute. Ask someone to time you.

Problem Set 1	Problem Set 2	Problem Set 3
12. 9 * 9	**27.** 96 / 8	**42.** 72 / 9
13. 36 / 9	**28.** 9 * 11	**43.** 8 * 11
14. 10 * 7	**29.** 54 / 9	**44.** 36 / 6
15. 11 * 4	**30.** 12 * 6	**45.** 8 / 4
16. 32 / 8	**31.** 9 * 5	**46.** 10 * 6
17. 11 * 8	**32.** 60 / 12	**47.** 121 / 11
18. 8 * 12	**33.** 6 * 8	**48.** 3 * 9
19. 10 * 11	**34.** 12 * 7	**49.** 7 * 7
20. 8 * 4	**35.** 18 / 2	**50.** 42 / 6
21. 60 / 10	**36.** 7 * 11	**51.** 84 / 12
22. 4 * 3	**37.** 54 / 6	**52.** 60 / 6
23. 40 * 30	**38.** 48 / 8	**53.** 9 * 7
24. 2 * 12	**39.** 6 * 6	**54.** 42 / 7
25. 32 / 4	**40.** 63 / 9	**55.** 6 * 7
26. 7 * 5	**41.** 120 / 12	**56.** 8 * 6

Use with or after Unit 7.   Write answers on a separate sheet of paper.

Mixed Practice Set 51

Rewrite the number sentences with parentheses to make them correct.

1. 9 * 12 − 3 = 81

2. 9 * 12 − 3 = 105

3. 15.8 = 2 * 6.5 + 2.8

4. 18.6 = 2 * 6.5 + 2.8

5. 7 * 1.1 + 4.2 × 12 = 58.1

6. 5 * 12 + 2 − 4 = 58

7. 5 * 12 + 2 − 4 = 66

8. 8140 = 110 * 50 + 24

Complete.

9. 4 ft = ■ in

10. 3 yd = ■ ft

11. 3 ft 5 in = ■ in

12. 2 yd 1 ft = ■ ft

13. 38 in = ■ ft ■ in

14. 9 ft = ■ yd

15. 26 ft = ■ yd ■ ft

16. 20 ft = ■ in

Use digits to write the following numbers.

17. seven million, eighty-four thousand

18. sixteen trillion, four hundred twenty-two million

19. two hundred sixty-seven million, five hundred thousand

Write the words for the following numbers.

20. 113,000,000

21. 2,905,100,000

22. 701,050,000

Write answers on a separate sheet of paper.   Use with or after Unit 8.

Mixed Practice Set 52

1. What kind of polygon is shown?
2. How many sides does it have?
3. If each side were 1.5 cm long, what would the perimeter be?

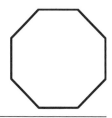

Complete the **What's My Rule?** tables.

4.

Rule	in	out
out = in + 38	9	
	12	
	15	
	25	
	100	

5.

Rule	in	out
	7	490
	10	700
		420
	11	
	3	210

6.

Rule	in	out
out = in − 108	80	
	160	
		90
	2400	
		1200

7.

Rule	in	out
	160	4
	440	11
		15
	800	
	30	$\frac{3}{4}$

Complete.

8. 140 minutes is the same as
   ■ hours and ■ minutes.

9. 63 hours is the same as
   ■ days and ■ hours.

10. 18 months is the same as
■ years and ■ months.

Write each number using digits.

11. eight million, four hundred twenty-three thousand, one hundred thirteen

12. five hundred seventy-two million, three hundred eighty-six thousand, eight hundred forty-nine

---

13. *Use the clues to complete the place-value puzzle.*

- Divide 88 by 11. Add 1 and write the result in the thousands place.

- Double the number in the thousands place and divide by 3. Write the result in the tens place.

- Multiply 4 ∗ 12. Subtract 42. Write the result in the hundreds place.

- Divide 63 by the number in the thousands place. Write the result in the ones place.

- Halve the number in the tens place. Add 1 and write the result in the ten-thousands place.

10,000s	1000s	100s	10s	1s

Solve.

14. $2.20 ∗ 5 = ■

15. 72 = 9 × ■

16. 4.2 + 2.3 = ■

17. 5 ∗ ■ = $3.50

18. ■ ÷ 1200 = 60

19. 28.0 − 6.4 = ■

20. 60 × ■ = 4200

21. ■ ÷ 36 = 20

Mixed Practice Set 53

In the numeral 28,490, the 8 stands for 8000.

1. What does the 4 stand for?

2. What does the 2 stand for?

3. What does the 9 stand for?

4. What does the 0 stand for?

Tell whether each number sentence is true or false.

5. $14 + 8 = 22$ **6.** $65 - 12 = 54$

7. $18 = 39 - 14$ **8.** $74 = 26 + 48$

Complete the frames-and-arrows problems.

9.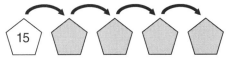

10.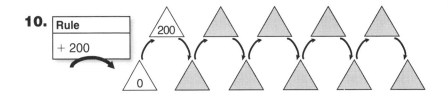

11.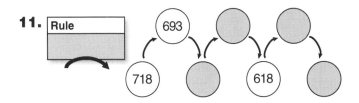

Mixed Practice Set 54

Write the value of the digit 8 in the numerals below.

1. 589

2. 87,402

3. 719,538

4. 482,391

5. 8,946,326

Use digits to write the following numbers.

6. seventy-four million, nine thousand, sixty-four

7. nineteen and sixty-eight hundredths

8. four hundred nine and eight hundred twenty-seven thousandths

---

Write the words for the following numbers.

9. 22.948

10. 174,480,900

11. 653.549

Make a name-collection box for each number below. Use as many different numbers and operations as you can.

Example:

538,000
538 × 1000
$\frac{1,076,000}{2}$
1,000,000 − 462,000

12. 935,000

13. 5,760,500

14. 318,450

Mixed Practice Set 54 *(continued)*

Fill in the missing numbers on the number lines below.
Follow these steps:

Step 1 Subtract the first number on the number line from the last number.

Step 2 Count the number of intervals (1 less than the total number of marks on the line).

Step 3 Divide the answer to Step 1 by the answer to Step 2. This is the number by which to count.

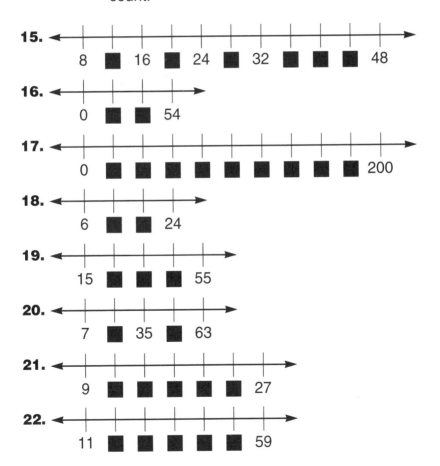

15. 8 ▪ 16 ▪ 24 ▪ 32 ▪ ▪ ▪ 48

16. 0 ▪ ▪ 54

17. 0 ▪ ▪ ▪ ▪ ▪ ▪ ▪ ▪ ▪ 200

18. 6 ▪ ▪ 24

19. 15 ▪ ▪ ▪ 55

20. 7 ▪ 35 ▪ 63

21. 9 ▪ ▪ ▪ ▪ ▪ 27

22. 11 ▪ ▪ ▪ ▪ ▪ 59

Mixed Practice Set 55

1. Make 5000s.

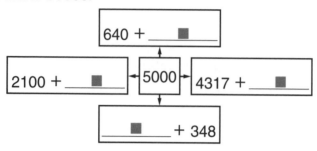

---

2. *Use the clues to complete the place-value puzzle.*

- Multiply 8 × 12. Subtract 90. Write the result in the hundreds place.
- Triple the number in the hundreds place and then halve. Write the result in the millions place.
- Divide 77 by 11. Add 1 and write the result in the hundred-thousands place.
- Double the number in the millions place and divide by 6. Write the result in the tens place.
- Add 2 to the number in the tens place. Write the result in the ten-thousands place.
- Divide 9 by the number in the millions place. Write the result in the ones place and the thousands place.

1,000,000s	100,000s	10,000s	1000s	100s	10s	1s

Solve.

3. $5.50 * 5 = ■

4. 80 = 8 * ■

5. 4.9 + 7.3 = ■

6. 4 × ■ = $2.40

7. ■ ÷ 180 = 30

8. 9.15 − 3.07 = ■

Mixed Practice Set 56

Complete the missing factors.

1. $70 * \blacksquare = 2100$

2. $\blacksquare * 4 = 360$

3. $\blacksquare * 80 = 6400$

4. $12 \times \blacksquare = 960$

5. $40 * \blacksquare = 480$

6. $\blacksquare * 50 = 3500$

7. $6 \times \blacksquare = 360$

8. $\blacksquare * 7 = 840$

Estimate the total cost.

9. 2 tape dispensers that cost $4.65 each

10. 12 magazines that cost $2.99 each

11. 9 scissors that cost 45¢ each

Solve.

12.
$$\begin{array}{r} 739 \\ + 372 \\ \hline \end{array}$$

13.
$$\begin{array}{r} 15 \\ + 938 \\ \hline \end{array}$$

14.
$$\begin{array}{r} 629 \\ - 419 \\ \hline \end{array}$$

15.
$$\begin{array}{r} 340 \\ \times 8 \\ \hline \end{array}$$

16.
$$\begin{array}{r} 17 \\ \times 9 \\ \hline \end{array}$$

17.
$$\begin{array}{r} 6382 \\ + 1826 \\ \hline \end{array}$$

18.
$$\begin{array}{r} 1856 \\ - 57 \\ \hline \end{array}$$

19.
$$\begin{array}{r} 240 \\ - 110 \\ \hline \end{array}$$

20.
$$\begin{array}{r} 160 \\ \times 4 \\ \hline \end{array}$$

21.
$$\begin{array}{r} 833 \\ + 284 \\ \hline \end{array}$$

22.
$$\begin{array}{r} 918 \\ + 193 \\ \hline \end{array}$$

23.
$$\begin{array}{r} 388 \\ - 63 \\ \hline \end{array}$$

24. Students started their tests at 9:25 A.M. The teacher told them they had $\frac{1}{2}$ hour to complete the exam. What time did they stop?

Mixed Practice Set 56 (continued)

Solve these problems mentally.

25. 76,432 − 1000

26. 76,432 − 100

27. 76,432 − 10,000

28. 76,432 − 10

29. Write the largest number you can using the following digits only once.

6, 4, 0, 1, 9, 4, 2, 3, 2

*Complete the **What's My Rule?** table.*

30.

Rule	in	out
out = in − 16	65	
	43	
		9
	82	
	114	

Write the amounts.

31. Ⓠ Ⓠ Ⓠ Ⓓ Ⓓ Ⓓ Ⓓ Ⓝ Ⓟ Ⓟ Ⓟ Ⓟ Ⓟ

32. $1 $1 Ⓠ Ⓠ Ⓠ Ⓓ Ⓓ Ⓓ Ⓓ
Ⓝ Ⓟ Ⓟ

33. $5 $1 $1 $1 $1 Ⓠ Ⓠ Ⓠ Ⓠ
Ⓝ Ⓝ Ⓝ

34. $100 $100 $20 $5 $1 $1 $1
Ⓠ Ⓠ Ⓠ Ⓠ Ⓠ

Mixed Practice Set 57

Tell whether each number sentence is true or false.

1. $19 + (9 * 7) = 82$ **2.** $56 = (8 * 5) + 13$

3. $14 + (15 * 7) = 119$ **4.** $24 - (72 / 9) = 16$

5. Order these numbers from smallest to largest.

   411.8   8.04   108.004   4,120.08   42,084.1

Solve.

6. $\begin{array}{r} 3857 \\ -\ 2432 \end{array}$ **7.** $\begin{array}{r} 9427 \\ \times\ 100 \end{array}$ **8.** $\begin{array}{r} 367 \\ -\ 46 \end{array}$ **9.** $\begin{array}{r} 29 \\ \times\ 4 \end{array}$

10. $\begin{array}{r} 28 \\ \times\ 8 \end{array}$ **11.** $\begin{array}{r} 740 \\ \times\ 6 \end{array}$ **12.** $\begin{array}{r} 215 \\ \times\ 7 \end{array}$ **13.** $\begin{array}{r} 3820 \\ +\ 2195 \end{array}$

14. Four people are going to share $118 equally.

   a. How many $10 bills does each person get?

   b. How many dollars are left to share?

   c. How many $1 bills does each person get?

   d. How many dollars are left to share?

   e. If the leftover money is shared equally, how many cents does each person get?

   f. What is the total amount of money each person gets?

   g. Write a number model for this problem.

15. Eight people are going to share $144 equally.

   a. How many $100 bills does each person get?

   b. How many $10 bills does each person get?

   c. How many dollars are left to share?

   d. How many $1 bills does each person get?

   e. What is the total amount of money each person gets?

   f. Write a number model for this problem.

16. Thirteen people are going to share $1365.65 equally.

   a. How many $100 bills does each person get?

   b. How much money is left to share?

   c. How many $10 bills does each person get?

   d. How much money is left to share?

   e. How many $1 bills does each person get?

   f. How much money is left over?

   g. If the leftover money is shared equally, how many cents does each person get?

   h. What is the total amount of money each person gets?

   i. Write a number model for this problem.

17. Karl has 62 marbles in his collection. Two are solid white, 6 are blue, and 9 are red. The rest are multicolored. How many marbles are multicolored?

Write the next three numbers in the pattern.

18. 0.5, 0.8, 1.1

19. 3.2, 3.7, 4.2

20. 8, 7.8, 7.6

21. 1.01, 1.02, 1.03

Mixed Practice Set 58

Rita checked the price of 1 pound of margarine at 5 different grocery stores. The prices she found were 85¢, 98¢, $1.09, 75¢, $1.08.

1. What is the maximum price?

2. What is the minimum price?

3. What is the range of prices?

4. What is the median price?

5. What is the mean (average) price?

Write two equivalent fractions for each of the following numbers.

6. $\frac{2}{11}$ **7.** $\frac{6}{7}$

8. $\frac{14}{15}$ **9.** $\frac{21}{30}$

10. $\frac{18}{9}$ **11.** $\frac{50}{100}$

12. $\frac{1}{9}$ **13.** $\frac{6}{4}$

14. Bruce, Bobbi, and Bryan are the three children in the Brown family. Use the following clues to find each one's age.

- Each of the older children is twice as old as the next younger child.

- The oldest is 12 years old.

- Bobbi is not the youngest.

- Bruce is half the age of Bryan.

Mixed Practice Set 58 *(continued)*

In each set of problems below, do as many exercises as you can in one minute. Ask someone to time you.

Problem Set 1	Problem Set 2	Problem Set 3
15. $14 - 6$	**30.** $84 / 7$	**45.** $72 / 6$
16. $7 / 7$	**31.** $12 * 11$	**46.** $44 / 4$
17. $96 / 8$	**32.** $7 + 18$	**47.** $121 - 11$
18. $4 * 111$	**33.** $3 * 8$	**48.** $9 * 9$
19. $11 - 4$	**34.** $4 * 10$	**49.** $144 / 12$
20. $12 + 5$	**35.** $11 * 4$	**50.** $7 * 8$
21. $14 + 8$	**36.** $3 * 11$	**51.** $4 * 70$
22. $12 - 7$	**37.** $12 + 9$	**52.** $144 / 12$
23. $54 / 9$	**38.** $4 * 7$	**53.** $21 - 3$
24. $9 * 12$	**39.** $11 + 11$	**54.** $55 + 5$
25. $14 / 7$	**40.** $81 / 9$	**55.** $6 * 7$
26. $24 / 3$	**41.** $54 / 6$	**56.** $9 * 9$
27. $5 + 6$	**42.** $50 + 60$	**57.** $500 + 600$
28. $18 / 2$	**43.** $40 / 10$	**58.** $32 / 8$
29. $4 * 80$	**44.** $27 / 3$	**59.** $36 / 9$

Write answers on a separate sheet of paper.   Use with or after Unit 9.

Mixed Practice Set 59

Solve.

1. 415
  × 30

2. 967
  − 58

3. 371
  − 47

4. 850
  + 380

5. 5382
  + 9381

6. 1940
  + 7629

7. 76
  × 50

8. 593
  + 8173

9. 1600
  − 101

10. $(100 + 70) * 4$

11. $56 - (9 * 4)$

12. $280 + 190 + 640$

13. How much is $\frac{1}{4}$ of 20¢?

14. How much is $\frac{1}{5}$ of 45¢?

15. How much is $\frac{1}{6}$ of 24¢?

16. How much is $\frac{1}{2}$ of 64¢?

17. How much is $\frac{1}{3}$ of 27¢?

18. How much is $\frac{1}{10}$ of $3.40?

---

19. *Use the clues to write a ten-digit number.*

- Write the result of 280 / 70 in the ten-thousands place.

- Multiply 6 * 7. Subtract 39. Write the result in the ten-millions place.

- Triple the number in the ten-millions place. Write the result in the hundred-thousands place.

- Subtract the number in the ten-thousands place from the number in the hundred-thousands place. Write the result in the billions place.

- Divide 80 by 10. Write the result in the rest of the places.

Mixed Practice Set 60

Who am I?

1. Clue 1: I am less than 10.

Clue 2: I am an even number.

Clue 3: If you subtract me from 7, the result is 3.

2. Clue 1: I am less than 100.

Clue 2: The sum of my digits is 16.

Clue 3: I am a multiple of 8.

3. Su was playing *Name That Number.* He drew 2, 5, 6, 8, 9. The target number was 16. Su made 16 with the 2, 6, and 8 cards: 2 + 6 + 8. Try to make 16 using more than three cards.

4. Order these numbers from smallest to largest.

0.5   0.05   50.005   0.15   1.51

Rewrite the number sentences with parentheses to make them correct.

5. $9 * 9 - 4 = 77$ **6.** $28 = 4 + 3 * 8$

7. $34 - 12 - 14 = 8$ **8.** $34 - 18 + 17 = -1$

9. $5 * 5 + 3 * 11 = 440$ **10.** $152 = 12 * 8 + 56$

11. $8 * 2 + 8 * 9 = 720$ **12.** $95 = 5 * 20 + 75 - 80$

Mixed Practice Set 60 (continued)

Complete the **What's My Rule?** tables.

13.

Rule	in	out
out = in − 55	83	
	75	
	114	
		−45
	15	

14.

Rule	in	out
	8	40
	14	46
		58
	35	
	43	75

Solve.

15.   9200
     − 427

16.   1834
     − 621

17.   3631
     + 7915

18.   6128
     − 3547

19.   8
     × 7000

20. 9)7200

21.   9000
     + 14,000

22.   946
     − 70

23.   1800
     − 300

24. 6)54,000

25.   7
     × 630

26. 8)5,600

Use with or after Unit 9.   Write answers on a separate sheet of paper.

Mixed Practice Set 61

1. Tom wants to enter the number 37 on his calculator, but the [7] key is broken. However, he can get 37 by entering 6 * 6 + 1.

Find two other ways to make 37 without using the [7] key. Try to use different numbers and operations.

The following totals came up when Tina threw two dice.

6, 5, 3, 8, 2, 6, 9, 4, 11, 6, 6, 4, 8, 6

2. What is the maximum?　　**3.** What is the minimum?

4. What is the range?　　**5.** What is the median?

6. What is the mode?　　**7.** What is the mean?

Fill in the missing numbers on the number lines.

8.

9.

10.

11.

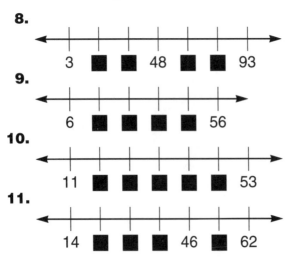

Mixed Practice Set 62

Write the number sentences with parentheses and solve.

1. Add 8.6 to the difference of 11.9 and 6.4.

2. Subtract the sum of 8 and 5.18 from 16.57.

3. Add 24 to the difference of 84.0 and 63.4.

4. Subtract the sum of 22 and 94.2 from 238.9.

Rewrite the number sentences with parentheses to make them correct.

5. 60 * 10 − 8 = 120

6. 9.2 = 8.2 + 3 / 3

7. 330 − 280 − 6 = 44

8. 8 − 12 + 9 = 5

9. 6 * 6 + 4 * 2 = 120

10. 310 = 40 * 6 + 70

11. 5 * 4 + 10 * 12 = 140

12. 85 = 6.5 * 2 + 9 * 8

Solve.

13. How many 11s in 121,000?

14. How many 6s in 36,000?

15. 54 * 200

16. 28 * 70

17. 300 * 9.0

18. 16.4 * 100

What are the next three numbers in each pattern?

19. −15, −10, −5,

20. 0.04, 0.06, 0.08,

21. 0.44, 0.68, 0.92

Julie and Pattie have 18 bananas, 16 oranges, and 20 apples. They are making bags of mixed fruit, with 4 pieces of fruit in each bag. They can put any combination of fruit in each bag.

22. How many bags can they make?

23. How many pieces of fruit will they have left over?

24. If they also had 7 pears, how many bags could they make?

25. How many nuts are there?

26. What fraction of the nuts are peanuts?

27. What fraction of the nuts are acorns?

28. What fraction of the nuts are almonds?

Mixed Practice Set 63

1. You start with a number. Triple it. Double the answer. You get 84. What number did you start with?

Write the following numbers with digits.

2. five hundred sixty-seven thousand, six hundred three

3. one hundred eighty million, one thousand

> 1 m = 100 cm
> 1 cm = 10 mm

Complete.

4. 20 cm = ■ mm   **5.** 5000 mm = ■ m

6. 20,000 mm = ■ cm   **7.** 2 m = ■ mm

8. 15 m = ■ cm   **9.** 2000 mm = ■ cm

When straight, a threadworm is about 306 mm long.

10. What is its length in cm?

11. What is the length in m?

Suppose you spun a paper clip on the base of the spinner below 180 times.

12. How many times would you expect it to land on red?

13. How many times would you expect it to land on blue?

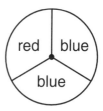

Mixed Practice Set 63 *(continued)*

Write number sentences for the following. Then tell whether they are true or false.

14. If 8 is subtracted from 24, the result is 16.

15. 6 is twice as much as 12.

16. 834 is more than 654.

17. Divide 86 by 2 and the result is 43.

18. If 98 is decreased by 16, the result is 84.

19. 27 is greater than the sum of 8 and 15.

20. Divide 126 by 14 and the result is 9.

21. 81 is the square number of 8.

22. Make 1000s.

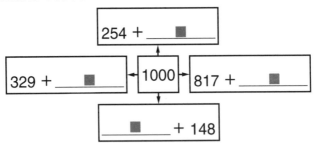

> Area = length (l) ∗ width (w)

Find the area, in square units, of each rectangle and then write the number model.

23.

24.

Mixed Practice Set 64

Rename the following fractions as decimals.

1. $\frac{1}{10}$ **2.** $\frac{2}{4}$ **3.** $\frac{6}{16}$ **4.** $\frac{6}{10}$

5. $\frac{500}{1000}$ **6.** $\frac{47}{100}$ **7.** $\frac{7}{8}$ **8.** $\frac{3}{4}$

9. $\frac{9}{16}$ **10.** $\frac{34}{100}$ **11.** $\frac{560}{1000}$ **12.** $\frac{18}{18}$

Tim found 5 different prices for notebooks: 35¢, $1.15, $1.29, $2.18, $1.17.

13. What is the maximum price?

14. What is the minimum price?

15. What is the range of prices?

16. What is the median price?

17. What is the mean (average) price?

Write the digit in the thousandths place.

18. 9.429   **19.** 4.920   **20.** 1.843

21. 1.674   **22.** 0.926   **23.** 5.5831

Solve.

24. $412 + 375 = $ ■   **25.** $189 + 413 = $ ■

26. $908 - 170 = $ ■   **27.** $3492 - 1804 = $ ■

28. $60 = 3600 \div $ ■   **29.** $235 - $ ■ $ = 81$

Mixed Practice Set 64 *(continued)*

30.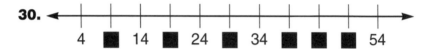
4 ■ 14 ■ 24 ■ 34 ■ ■ ■ 54

31.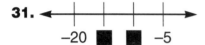
−20 ■ ■ −5

32.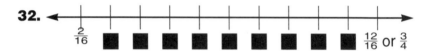
$\frac{2}{16}$ ■ ■ ■ ■ ■ ■ ■ ■ ■ $\frac{12}{16}$ or $\frac{3}{4}$

33.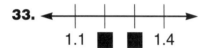
1.1 ■ ■ 1.4

34.
25 ■ ■ ■ 125

35.
8 ■ ■ 32 ■ 48

36.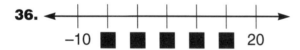
−10 ■ ■ ■ ■ ■ 20

37.
−8 ■ ■ ■ ■ ■ 4

38.
0 ■ ■ ■ ■ ■ ■ ■ ■ ■ 1000

39.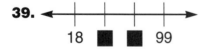
18 ■ ■ 99

Write answers on a separate sheet of paper. Use with or after Unit 10.

Mixed Practice Set 65

Copy and then complete the Powers of 10 Table.

The Powers of 10 Table

Millions	Hundred-Thousands	Ten-Thousands	Thousands	Hundreds	Tens	Ones
1,000,000				100		1
10 [100,000s]			10 [100s]			10 [0.1s]
		10*10*10*10				
	10^5		10^3			▓
						10^0

Mixed Practice Set 66

1. Which of the following numbers are square numbers?

35   10   49   54   81

Tell whether the following number sentences are true or false.

2. $15 + (4 \times 5) = 55$

3. $(5 \times 8) - 4 = 46$

4. $15 = (24 \div 6) \times 3$

5. $(36 \div 6) \div 2 < 5$

6. $29 < 40 - (9 + 11)$

Complete the frames-and-arrows problems.

7.

Rule
$+ 100$

Rule
$- 50$

65

8.

Rule
$\times 5$

Rule
$\div 2$

40

Mixed Practice Set 66 *(continued)*

Solve.

9. $540 / 6 = \blacksquare$

10. $250 \times 80 = \blacksquare$

11. $640 = 8 * \blacksquare$

12. $20 * 300 = \blacksquare$

13. $60 * \blacksquare = 2400$

14. $\blacksquare \div 50 = 6$

15. $5600 / 700 = \blacksquare$

16. $360 \times \blacksquare = 7200$

17. $\blacksquare \div 5 = 35$

18. $9 * 200 = \blacksquare$

19. $540 \div \blacksquare = 90$

20. $110 * 120 = \blacksquare$

21. How much is $\frac{1}{8}$ of 32¢?

22. How much is $\frac{4}{9}$ of 54¢?

23. How much is $\frac{1}{10}$ of 80¢?

24. How much is $\frac{1}{3}$ of 90¢?

25. How much is $\frac{1}{5}$ of $2.20?

26. How much is $\frac{2}{3}$ of 27¢?

27. How much money, without tax, will I need for 3 audio tapes that cost $1.69 each?

28. How many dollars in 17 five-dollar bills?

29. The soccer game was over at 4:40 P.M. It had lasted 25 minutes. What time did the game start?

Mixed Practice Set 67

1. Make 8000s.

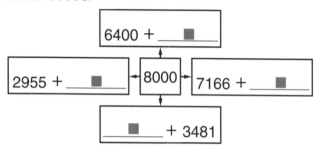

Rename the following numbers as percents.

2. $\frac{1}{4}$ **3.** 0.75   **4.** 1.00   **5.** $\frac{57}{100}$

6. $\frac{3}{20}$ **7.** $\frac{10}{25}$ **8.** 0.4   **9.** $\frac{37.5}{100}$

10. $\frac{4}{5}$ **11.** 1.125   **12.** $\frac{765}{1000}$ **13.** $\frac{6}{18}$

> 1 km = 1000 m; 1 m = 100 cm
> 1 cm = 10 mm

Complete.

14. 2 km = ■ cm   **15.** 25,000 mm = ■ m

16. 1800 m = ■ km   **17.** 30 km = ■ m

18. 3.3 km = ■ mm   **19.** 670 cm = ■ mm

---

20. *Who Am I?*

Clue 1: I am a whole number less than 5.

Clue 2: If you multiply me by 3, the result is more than 10.

Write answers on a separate sheet of paper.   Use with or after Unit 10.

Mixed Practice Set 68

The following sentences have been written without placing decimal points in the numbers. Find the wrong number in each sentence and place a decimal—and zeros if necessary—to make it correct.

1. In 1936, Jessie Owens ran the 100-meter dash in 103 seconds.

2. In that same year, the U.S. won the 2-man bobsled race in 5 minutes, 2929 seconds.

3. It costs $1499 for a 1-year subscription to National Geographic World Magazine.

4. The U.S. Postal Service charges $32 to mail a 1-ounce letter.

5. With $12, Alice was able to buy 8 gallons of gas at a rate of $15 per gallon.

Solve.

6.
$$\begin{array}{r} 14.8 \\ + 12.2 \end{array}$$

7.
$$\begin{array}{r} 113.24 \\ + 7.56 \end{array}$$

8.
$$\begin{array}{r} 26 \\ \times 4 \end{array}$$

9.
$$\begin{array}{r} 1.80 \\ \times 7 \end{array}$$

10.
$$\begin{array}{r} 0.196 \\ \times 0 \end{array}$$

11.
$$\begin{array}{r} 72.1 \\ + 19.3 \end{array}$$

12.
$$\begin{array}{r} 1.25 \\ + 6.43 \end{array}$$

13.
$$\begin{array}{r} 12.96 \\ - 11.41 \end{array}$$

14.
$$\begin{array}{r} 11.1 \\ \times 9 \end{array}$$

15.
$$\begin{array}{r} 1.85 \\ - .38 \end{array}$$

16.
$$\begin{array}{r} 5037 \\ + 8632 \end{array}$$

17.
$$\begin{array}{r} 962 \\ - 421 \end{array}$$

18. If 1 block is 200 meters long, how many meters will you run in 8 blocks?

19. There are 5280 feet in one mile. How many feet are in 10 miles?

Find the percent of the following.

20. 70% of 10   **21.** 25% of 80   **22.** 75% of 12

23. 50% of 64   **24.** 24% of 25   **25.** 150% of 22

26. 80% of 50   **27.** 90% of 100   **28.** 33% of 1000

29. 12% of 200   **30.** 6% of 50   **31.** 15% of 20

Solve these problems mentally.

32. 934,167 − 1000 = ■   **33.** 934,167 − 100 = ■

34. 934,167 − 10,000 = ■   **35.** 934,167 − 10 = ■

36. *Use the clues to build a four-digit number.*

- Write 5 in the hundreds place.
- Double 14; divide it by 4. Write the result in the ones place.
- Subtract 3 from the digit in the ones place. Write the result in the tens place.
- Write a number in the tenths place so that the sum of all four digits in this number is 22.

*Complete the **What's My Rule?** tables.*

37.

Rule	in	out
out = in * 50	7	
	9	
	12	
	14	
	35	

38.

Rule	in	out
	7	$10\frac{1}{2}$
	10	$13\frac{1}{2}$
		20
	$19\frac{1}{2}$	
	$21\frac{1}{2}$	25

Mixed Practice Set 69

Solve.

1. 18
    × 42

2. 12
    × 35

3. 417
    × 8

4. 9275
    + 1897

5. 5108
    + 382

6. 932
    + 4892

7. 4824
    − 393

8. 2853
    − 234

---

9. *Use the clues to build a seven-digit number.*

- Multiply 7 ∗ $\frac{1}{7}$. Write the result in the ones place.

- Double the number in the ones place and write the result in the hundreds place.

- Subtract 25 from the number of days in January. Write the result in the millions place.

- Halve the number in the millions place and write the result in the thousands place.

- Multiply 3 by itself. Write the result in the tens place.

- Subtract the number in the ones place from the number in the thousands place. Write the result in the hundred-thousands place.

- Divide 24 by the number in the thousands place. Write the result in the ten-thousands place.

10. What time does the clock show?
Write your answer to the nearest
minute.

11. What time will it be in
35 minutes?

12. What time will it be in
88 minutes?

---

13. *Write the largest number you can using the following digits only once.*

0,   5,   3,   6,   9,   2,   3,   1,   7

Solve.

14. 274 * 5

15. 158 * 7

16. 236 * 30

17. 1,100,000 − 800,000

18. 353 − 243

19. 647 − 42

20. 32,000 + 18,000

21. 7394 + 294

22. 9365 − 7375

23. 40)‾640

24. 6)‾195

25. 13)‾390

26. 204 + 320 + 468

27. 472 + 492 + 395

Find the total cost for each of the following:

28. 14 pencils that cost 9¢ each

29. 9 scissors that cost $1.65 each

30. 4 books that cost $4.45 each

31. 11 rulers that cost $1.26 each

32. 4 pairs of shoes that cost $14.34 each

Mixed Practice Set 70

Use the following list of numbers to answer the questions.

5, 7, 3, 9, 11, 4, 5, 3, 10, 1, 5

1. Which number is the smallest?

2. Which number is the largest?

3. What is the difference between the smallest and largest numbers?

4. Which number appears most often?

Write <, > or = to make each number sentence true.

Reminder:
> greater than < less than = equal to

5. 47 + 63 ■ 22 + 74

6. 8 + 43 ■ 7 + 13 + 31

7. 85 + 33 ■ 81 + 35

8. 9 ∗ 12 ■ 404 / 4

9. 169 − 40 ■ 95 + 26

10. Order these numbers from smallest to largest.

$\frac{1}{4}$ $\frac{3}{6}$ $\frac{1}{10}$ $\frac{9}{12}$ $\frac{16}{16}$

Solve these problems mentally.

11. 1,458,304 − 1000

12. 1,458,304 − 100

13. 1,458,304 − 10,000

14. 1,458,304 − 1,000,000

15. 1,458,304 − 10

16. 1,458,304 − 100,000

Mixed Practice Set 70 (continued)

For each Fact Minute below, complete as many facts and fact extensions as you can in that minute.

Fact Minute 1	Fact Minute 2	Fact Minute 3
17. 4 * 8	**32.** 2 * 60	**47.** 9 – 6
18. 17 – 8	**33.** 16,000 – 8000	**48.** 21 / 7
19. 5 * 9	**34.** 54 / 9	**49.** 400 * 50
20. 120 / 60	**35.** 64,000 / 80	**50.** 5400 / 9
21. 3 * 8	**36.** 32 / 8	**51.** 2 * 600
22. 27 / 9	**37.** 27 / 3	**52.** 8 * 7
23. 7 * 4	**38.** 490 / 7	**53.** 60 * 80
24. 5 * 5	**39.** 2800 / 70	**54.** 400 / 5
25. 1200 / 40	**40.** 9 * 2	**55.** 1200 / 6
26. 6 * 30	**41.** 320,000 / 40	**56.** 60 * 60
27. 4 * 3	**42.** 28 / 7	**57.** 8 * 10
28. 40 * 3	**43.** 320 / 4	**58.** 6300 / 9
29. 80 * 3	**44.** 90 / 3	**59.** 3600 / 4
30. 3200 / 8	**45.** 4800 /6	**60.** 5400 / 90
31. 720 / 9	**46.** 800 * 300	**61.** 4200 / 6

Write answers on a separate sheet of paper.   Use with or after Unit 11.

Mixed Practice Set 71

Solve each number sentence by finding the value of the variable.

1. $A = (6 * 6) / 3$

2. $40 / B = 48 / 6$

3. $C = (20 + 6) \div 4$

4. $8 + (14 \times 3) = D$

Solve.

5. $45 * 3$

6. $58 * 11$

7. $340 * 4$

8. $290 * 5$

9. $670 * 3$

10. $334 * 12$

11. On Friday Mr. and Mrs. Castillo drove 165 miles. On Saturday they drove 317 miles. On Sunday they drove 274 miles. How many miles did they drive in all?

12. If their car gets 20 miles per gallon, about how many gallons of fuel did they use? Round to the nearest gallon.

13. You went to the mall with a $20 bill and three $1 bills. You spent $19.77 on groceries. You also spent $1.50 on bus fare each way. How much do you have left?

14. If you remove 3 gallons per day from a 50-gallon water tank, how long will it take to empty the tank? Use a fraction to express a portion of a day.

15. Draw two arrays that represent the number model $4 * 7 = 28$.

Mixed Practice Set 72

Answer the following questions. If the answer is a fraction, write it in simplest terms.

1. What part of the group of coins are pennies?

2. What part of the group of coins are nickels?

3. What part of the group of coins are dimes?

4. How much money is in the whole group?

5. If you took away $\frac{2}{3}$ of the nickels and $\frac{5}{6}$ of the pennies, how much money would be left?

---

6. What time does the clock show? Write your answer to the nearest minute.

7. What time will it be in 55 minutes?

8. What time will it be in 96 minutes?

9. What time was it 1 hour and 10 minutes ago?

Mixed Practice Set 72 *(continued)*

Try to reach the target number using any operations and as many of the given numbers as possible.

10. Target Number: 26
Numbers to Use: 5, 7, 4, 8, 12, 15

11. Target Number: 18
Numbers to Use: 1, 3, 4, 7, 12

12. Target Number: 27
Numbers to Use: 2, 3, 4, 14, 16

13. Target Number: 29
Numbers to Use: 3, 5, 6, 7, 11

Write the missing numbers.

14.

15.

16.

17.

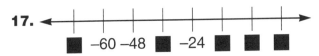

18.

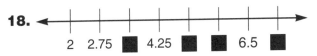

19.

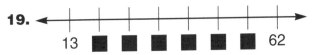

Mixed Practice Set 73

In the numeral 76.903, the 7 stands for 7 tens.

1. What does the 6 stand for?

2. What does the 9 stand for?

3. What does the 0 stand for?

4. What does the 3 stand for?

Write two multiplication and two division facts for each of the following.

5.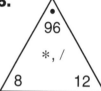

6.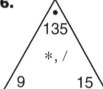

7.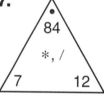

8.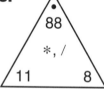

9.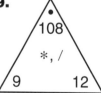

10.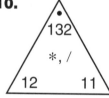

Mixed Practice Set 74

Solve.

1. Which temperature is colder, −17°C or −32°C?

2. Which is colder, +20°C or −13°C?

3. You have 62 cookies. You give 4 cookies to each of your friends until you run out of cookies. How many friends received cookies?

4. You have 62 cookies and you want to share them equally among you and 17 friends. How many will each person get?

Write the next three numbers in the pattern.

5. 23,610; 23,615; 23,620

6. 39.55, 39.50, 39.45

7. 151, 148, 145,

8. 1455, 1130, 805

Complete.

9. $10^2 = $ ■

10. $10^■ = 1000$

11. $10 * 10 * 10 * 10 * 10 * 10 = 10^■$

> Volume = length × width × height
> = area of base × height

Find the volume of each rectangular prism.

12. 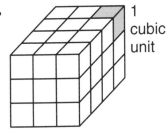 1 cubic unit

13.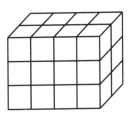

Mixed Practice Set 74 (continued)

Write the next three numbers in each pattern.

14. 80, 40, 0

15. 65, 70, 75

16. 24, 36, 48

17. 77, 88, 99

18. A number has

4 in the billions place

7 in the hundred-thousands place

5 in the ten-billions place

1 in the thousands place

6 in the hundred-millions place

0 in the rest of the places

Write the number.

Complete the **What's My Rule?** tables.

19.

Rule	in	out
out = in + 115	18	
	34	
		258
	48	
	90	

20.

Rule	in	out
out = in − 84	173	
	234	
		9
	67	
		−51

Mixed Practice Set 75

Write true or false for each number sentence.

1. 14 + 13 = 27

2. 6 * 9 = 48

3. 4 * 7 < 30

4. 41 − 25 = 18

5. 3 * 3 = 54 ÷ 6

6. 4 * (6 + 2) = 24

Solve.

7. How many 90s in 180,000?

8. How many 50s in 6500?

9. 52 * 210

10. 7600 * 3

11. 2400 * 7

12. 1900 * 30

13. Joe has 129 rocks in his collection. He has a rock polisher that can polish 10 rocks at a time. He has polished 5 batches of rocks. How many rocks are not polished?

Kathy has stickers to put up in her room. Some are glow-in-the-dark stars and moons, and some are bear stickers.

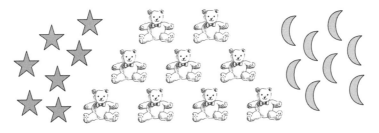

14. What part of the group are stars?

15. What part of the group are moons?

16. What part of the group are bears?

17. What part of the group are glow-in-the-dark?

Mixed Practice Set 75 *(continued)*

Write your own rate tables for the problems below. Then answer the questions.

Example: Richard's car travels about 25 miles on 1 gallon of gasoline.

miles	25	50	75	100	125	150
gallons	1	2	3	4	5	6

18. How far can the car travel on 6 gallons of gas?

19. At 125 miles, how many gallons have been used?

The Sweet Tooth Ice Cream factory can make 100 gallons of ice cream per day.

gallons	100	■	■	■	■	■	■
day	1	2	3	4	5	6	7

20. How many gallons can the factory make in a week?

21. How many gallons can it make in a year?

Rita is a seamstress. She can make 3 dresses in 2 hours.

dresses	3	■	■	■	■	■
hours	2	4	6	8	10	12

22. How many dresses can Rita make in an 8-hour day?

23. If she takes off an hour for lunch, how many dresses will she make?

Write <, >, or = to make a true number sentence.

24. 29 + 33 ■ 45 + 17   **25.** 20 + 30 + 40 ■ 35 + 55

26. 35 + 13 ■ 32 + 18   **27.** 130 − 18 ■ 55 × 2

28. 13 + 12 ■ 48 ÷ 2   **29.** 118 + 220 ■ 1000 − 692

Mixed Practice Set 76

Write the next three numbers in each pattern.

1. 9, 24, 39

2. 11, 7, 3

3. 45, 90, 135

4. 12, 2, –8

5. Roger, Susie, LeeAnn, and David all have a favorite sport. One likes swimming, one likes tennis, one likes basketball, and one likes baseball. Use the clues to find which sport each one likes.

- David doesn't like water.
- Both Roger and Susie like to hit a ball.
- Susie doesn't like to play a game with a net.

Which sport does each person like?

---

6. *Write the largest number you can using the following digits only once.*

6, 4, 0, 1, 9, 4, 2, 3, 2

---

*Complete the **What's My Rule?** tables.*

7.

Rule	in	out
out = in − 116	165	
	433	
		97
	82	
	114	

8.

Rule	in	out
out = in × 50	65	
	43	
		9
	15	
	109	

Mixed Practice Set 76 *(continued)*

Rename the following fractions as decimals.

9. $\frac{18}{100}$ **10.** $\frac{6}{10}$ **11.** $\frac{3}{10}$ **12.** $\frac{1}{3}$

13. $\frac{250}{1000}$ **14.** $\frac{47}{100}$ **15.** $\frac{4}{8}$ **16.** $\frac{1}{4}$

17. $\frac{6}{16}$ **18.** $\frac{42}{100}$ **19.** $\frac{182}{1000}$ **20.** $\frac{14}{18}$

Complete the frames-and-arrows problems.

21.

Rule
+ 65

22.

Rule
* 100

23.

Rule
/ 4

24.

Rule
* 100

Rule
− 200

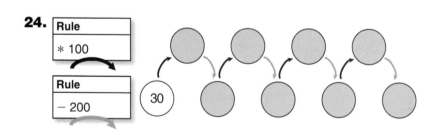

Mixed Practice Set 77

Find the percent of the following.

1. 34% of 50

2. 25% of 60

3. 15% of 35

4. 60% of 600

5. 1.5% of 20

6. 10% of 77

7. 5% of 20

8. 66% of 1000

9. 22% of 150

10. 45% of 900

11. 110% of 0

12. 200% of 93

Solve each number sentence by finding the value of the variable.

13. $A = (8 * 9) \div 3$

14. $64 / B = 32 \div 2$

15. $C = (23 + 9) \div 8$

16. $45 + (11 * 6) = D$

17. $43 - E = 80 / 2$

18. $F / 19 = 570$

19. $(60 - 18) \div 6 = G$

20. $(13 * 20) - H = 10^2$

Complete.

21. $10^4 = \blacksquare$

22. $10^{\blacksquare} = 100,000$

23. $600 = 6 * 10^{\blacksquare}$

24. $10 * 10 * 10 * 10 = 10^{\blacksquare}$

25. 10 to the eighth power $= \blacksquare$

26. $3.0 * 10^6 = \blacksquare$

27. 10 to the $\blacksquare$ power $= 1000$

Mixed Practice Set 78

Write your own rate tables for the problems below. Then answer the questions.

It takes Christie 3 minutes to read a page of her book.

minutes	3	■	■	■	■	■
pages	1	2	3	4	5	6

1. How many pages can she read in 15 minutes?

2. At this rate, how many pages will she read in 1/2 hour?

The cars on the freeway are traveling 55 miles per hour.

miles	55	■	■	■	■	■
hours	1	2	3	4	5	6

3. How far will they go in 5 hours?

4. About how long will it take to travel 300 miles?

Howard delivers 14 newspapers in 10 minutes.

papers	14	■	■	■	■	■
minutes	10	20	30	40	50	60

5. How many papers can Howard deliver in 1 hour?

6. How long will it take Howard to deliver the 70 papers on his route?

Tomatoes cost 65¢ a pound.

price	$1.30	■	■	■	■	■
pounds	2	4	6	8	10	12

7. How much do 10 pounds of tomatoes cost?

8. About how many pounds of tomatoes can you buy with $5.00?

Mixed Practice Set 78 *(continued)*

Solve.

9. 6234 + 384   **10.** 65 $*$ 12   **11.** 387 − 124

12. 1234 − 834   **13.** 5000 $\times$ 800   **14.** 2435 + 627

15. 2544 + 6335   **16.** 592 − 348   **17.** 540 − 164

18. 687 − 236   **19.** 332 − 140   **20.** 33 $*$ 81

21. 1294 + 5729   **22.** 600 $\times$ 50   **23.** 7025 + 3611

24. On Friday night, 345 people went to the cultural center for a dance. On Saturday night, 462 people went to a dance. How many people in all attended the dances on Friday and Saturday nights?

Rename the following numbers as percents.

25. $\frac{1}{8}$ **26.** 0.45   **27.** 2.00

28. $\frac{63}{100}$ **29.** $\frac{1}{20}$ **30.** $\frac{11}{25}$

31. 0.7   **32.** $\frac{9}{100}$ **33.** $\frac{5}{8}$

34. 3.4   **35.** $\frac{133}{1000}$ **36.** $\frac{2}{16}$

Mixed Practice Set 79

Solve.

1. 3465 + 6734	**2.** 253 + 246	**3.** 26 × 8	**4.** 83 × 3
5. 450 × 500	**6.** 1.78 + 7.517	**7.** 2.786 + 1.915	**8.** 121.94 − 60.25
9. 120 × 9000	**10.** 272 − 237	**11.** 2058 + 3217	**12.** 2622 − 895

13. You had $7.60 before you spent $2.95 for a book. How much money do you have now?

Make the number sentences true by inserting parentheses.

14. $4 - 4 * 7 = 0$ **15.** $4 - 4 * 7 = -24$

16. $45 \div 9 + 10 = 15$ **17.** $8 * 7 - 6 = 8$

18. $8 \times 7 - 6 = 50$ **19.** $13 = 5 + 24 \div 3$

---

20. *Use the clues to build a seven-digit number.*

- Divide 54 by 6. Subtract 5 and write the result in the ones place.

- Double the number in the ones place. Write the result in the hundreds place.

- Multiply 8 * 10. Subtract 75. Write the result in the hundred-thousands place.

- Halve the number in the ones place. Multiply by 3 and write the result in the millions place.

- Divide 28 by the number in the ones place. Write the result in the ten-thousands place.

- Write the number 3 in the remaining places.

Mixed Practice Set 80

1. Make 100s.

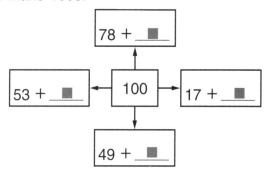

Suppose you spun a paper clip on the base of the spinner below 540 times.

2. How many times would you expect it to land on red?

3. How many times would you expect it to land on blue?

4. How many times would you expect it to land on green?

5. How many times would you expect it to land on yellow?

---

6. A square number is the product of a number multiplied by itself. For example, 81 is a square number because 9 ∗ 9 = 81. Which of the following numbers are square numbers?

14   25   90   100   1000

Mixed Practice Set 80 *(continued)*

Solve.

7.   253
      $\times\ 4$

8.   235
      $-\ 725$

9.   2525
      $-\ 727$

10.   8000
       $+\ 15{,}000$

11.   5250
       $+\ 1205$

12.   3104
       $+\ 1832$

13.   249
       $\times\ 20$

14.   151
       $+\ 553$

15.   1325
       $-\ 944$

16. $(50 + 20) \times 4000$

17. $2900 - (50 \times 40)$

18. $632 + 363 + 363$

19. $1600 - (7200 \div 90)$

Solve the problems.

20. 138 people came to the school's pancake breakfast. Tickets cost $5 per person. How much money did the pancake breakfast make?

21. The school paid $143 for the food that was served. The people who ran the breakfast volunteered their time. How much did the breakfast make, after expenses?

22. An office clerk made 1267 photocopies on Monday. On Tuesday, the same clerk made 1209 copies. On Wednesday, he made 382 copies. How many copies did he make in all?